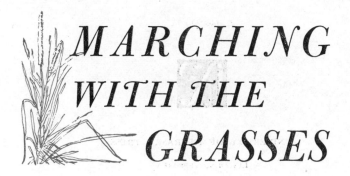

MARCHING
WITH THE
GRASSES

RAYMOND J. POOL

1948

UNIVERSITY OF NEBRASKA PRESS

Preface

THE AUTHOR BELIEVES THAT THIS BOOK SHOULD APPEAL TO A HOST of people who wish to develop a broad background for the appreciation of world affairs or to enlarge their understanding of a group of unique organisms, which are of the greatest importance to man. The book will particularly interest students and teachers in the fields of general science, botany, agriculture, biology, and also in those of agronomy, geography, geopolitics, sociology, commerce, and history. It presents material without which the story of civilization cannot claim to be told completely.

Students, farmers, and readers in general will find here an introduction to the global distribution, history, evolution, and the general social and economic significance of the wild grasses and their cultivated relatives upon which man is dependent. An appreciation of the world-wide nature of these plants and their many distinctive products should help to develop a more complete understanding of this "one world" of ours. This should blend quite naturally into the expanding international point of view that has been developing in this country for some years. If the author's efforts serve to contribute even in a small way to this noble end, they will have been well expended.

The preparation of a volume of this kind demands that the author draw freely from publications, both technical and popular, and utilize suggestions and materials that have been contributed by a host of colleagues at home and abroad. It is quite impossible to acknowledge such a varied and very real debt other than in this general way. Several specific contributions have been credited at the point where they are used, but many others must go unidentified. We are grateful for the privilege of reproducing the drawings of many grasses that have appeared in publications of the United States Department of Agriculture, especially from Hitchcock's *The Genera of Grasses of the United States*. Statistical data which are mostly shown in tables and in maps have also been derived from the same Department, particularly from *Agricultural Statistics for 1946, The Bureau of Agricultural Economics,* and *The Division of Cereal Crops and Diseases*. The latter Division has also furnished certain photographs which are noted in

v

the respective legends. The *U. S. Soil Conservation Service* has also supplied certain photographs which are acknowledged under the respective figures. The agricultural reports of various nations and states have been drawn upon for data and information that have been worked into the text.

RAYMOND J. POOL

Lincoln, Nebraska

August 30, 1947.

Contents

Figures

ix

Tables

Introduction

As these lines are written the world is threatened by famine, the magnitude and the consequences of which are terrifying. More people are now desperately hungry than ever before in the long struggle of man toward a better life. Added to the widespread acute aspects of near starvation are those more insidious and difficult to diagnose, yet all the more real and pitiful conditions that we now describe under the caption of "hidden hunger." The latter is relieved only by certain vitamins and minerals. Many of these substances are present in minute quantities in food and they are often supplied by the whole-grain foods. The bulk of these essentials in human diet is relatively small but we now know that they are indispensable for good health and vigorous application to the tasks of life.

The nations of the earth are blindly groping hither and yon in an effort to avert the threatening collapse of society and civilization. This is all the more tragic since it comes at the very moment when our time has been widely acclaimed as the most enlightened age of mankind. The horrors of the present state of affairs are chiefly due, of course, to the globe-engulfing war that has so lately ended, and the severe failure of the important crops in various lands, plus the seeming inability of the political, social, and economic leaders of the world to learn the primary lessons that always confront nations during the period of rehabilitation and reconstruction that follows such a crisis.

The war has once more, and on an unusually broad scale, torn the veneer of security entirely free from the face of world society and exposed to the people of all lands and conditions the staggering truth that it is still only a step from prosperity to ruin, from abundance to famine. Men of all colors and classes still labor behind the uncertain protection of an exceedingly thin veil that we call civilization. Millions are today learning the simple biological lesson that men live abundantly and happily only in close dependence upon the many direct and indirect contributions of the grasses. When they hunger they cry for rice, for wheat, for corn, for sugar, and for the products of our livestock that are formed on a diet of grasses.

Even the most fortunate of men normally move within a very narrow and precarious zone of abundance. The transition from a happy and well-fed nation to a hungry and unsocial one may be but a step, even in peace time, and even in the most productive and progressive nations. A widespread crop failure, especially of any one or more of the three major cereals, or the stunning blows of a world war teach us this lesson in a most uncomfortable and convincing manner. When, for any reason, the production and free flow of the wholesome energizing foods that the world of men and livestock reaps from the grasses become pathological or seriously impaired, man goes hungry, he becomes unsocial and radical, he starves, he dies by the millions, society is impoverished, and the onward march of civilization is halted.

Why cannot man profit from the vivid lessons of the past in these matters? The solution to the problem is not to be found in the field of botanical science. We must look to a scientific social and economic order for the final answer to this age-old dilemma. More of our people should learn to understand, and more fully to appreciate, what the biological sciences have contributed to cushion the burdens of man, to extend his span of life, and to equip him with a somewhat surer food supply which may sustain him in such times of near world collapse.

The following chapters present but a summary of one of the most significant and fundamental patterns that, with a few others (mostly spiritual), constitutes the central theme that has sustained and inspired man in his long upward struggle toward a more perfect life on earth. In a sense the book constitutes a brief introduction to the rôle that the wild and cultivated grasses have played and are now playing in the slow evolution and differentiation of human society. Americans have a peculiarly vital interest in this story. Basically our agriculture is of the grain and livestock type. Our corn and wheat are ideally adapted to the natural grassland climate and soils of our continent. Eons of time have been required for nature to perfect that *combination of climate, soils, animals,* and *plants* which we call our *native prairie.* This is the original heritage of every American.

Our narrative is presented with the hope that those who study it may gain a more vivid and lasting impression of the truly vital and global importance of man's best friends in the great world of plant life, the GRASSES.

CHAPTER 1

The Family Traits of the Grasses

THE TRUE GRASSES CONSTITUTE A HIGHLY VARIED AND UNIQUELY SPE-cialized group of flowering plants. They are included in a clearly defined natural family which is technically known as the *Gramineae*. This is the most important group of all of the hundreds of types, that together complete the extremely varied creation that botanists have recognized as the flora of the globe. No other natural group of organisms is more valuable or important to man. When the grasses thrive, man is well fed and rich. When the crop of wild and domesticated grasses fails, man is hungry, he may become pauperized, he may starve. There is no real substitute for the food values that mankind secures from the grasses.

The closest relatives of the grasses include the Sedges, *Cyperaceae*, and the Rushes, *Juncaceae*. Many members of these groups are often associated in nature with the grasses and they are so grass-like that they are commonly mistaken for true grasses by the uninitiated. Somewhat more distant relatives of the grasses that we may mention are the Lilies, *Liliaceae*, Palms, *Palmaceae*, Callas or Aroids, *Araceae*, and even the Pineapples, *Bromeliaceae*, Bananas, *Musaceae*, Irises, *Iridaceae*, and those most aristocratic of all flowering plants, the Orchids, *Orchidaceae*. These extraordinary and outstanding groups are included within one of the two major series of flowering plants that are widely distributed over the globe and known to botanists as the *Monocotyledons*.

The large natural family *Gramineae* includes about 600 genera, of which some 145 occur in the United States. These are grouped into twelve or fourteen *tribes* each of which in turn includes many of the genera. There are now about 6,000 species of grasses known to the botanists of the world, of which about 1,500 occur in North America. To these must be added thousands of varieties of cultivated grasses including the cereals, sugar cane, sorghums, and many forage plants.

1

All of the tribes are represented by genera and species that are found in the United States. Some of the more common tribes are as follows: *Festuceae,* the Fescue, Brome, and Blue Grasses; *Hordeae,* the Wheat, Rye, and Barley Grasses; *Aveneae,* the Oat Grasses; *Agrostideae,* the Timothy and Muhly Grasses; *Chlorideae,* Buffalo Grass and the Grama Grasses; *Oryzeae,* Rice Grasses; *Paniceae,* the Millet Grasses; *Andropogoneae,* Sorghum and Sugar Cane; *Maydeae,* Indian Corn; *Bambuseae,* the Bamboos.

The grasses display a surprising variety of form and size as well as myriads of anatomical details that are associated with their vegetative bodies and their floral structures. They are annual or perennial and their flowering stems are mostly erect or divergent. The aerial shoots of many of the perennials are annual, that is, they die back and are replaced by new shoots each year, but the underground parts live on for several years. Many species have widely spreading, prostrate, aerial stems, and others have more or less well-developed and extensive underground stems (Fig. 1). Grasses are equipped with fibrous roots that are usually much branched and widely spreading. The varied

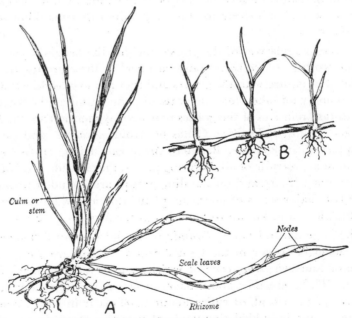

FIG. 1. The ribbon-like leaves and rhizomes of Quack Grass. A, mature plant with rhizomes showing scaly leaves; B, young plant showing how new erect shoots arise at the joints *(from Pool, after Matthews).*

combinations of spreading aerial and subterranean stems (*stolons* and *rhizomes* (Figs. 1, 83, 84) and myriads of finely divided, fibrous roots serve to anchor the grasses very firmly in place in the soil. The roots of single plants of certain species of grasses would total a length of several miles if the individual roots and all of their branches were to be dug up and placed end to end. Such structures endow grasses with an incomparable power to hold the soil in position against the insidious and destructive forces of wind and water that sweep over the surface of the earth. Herein lies the biological explanation of the

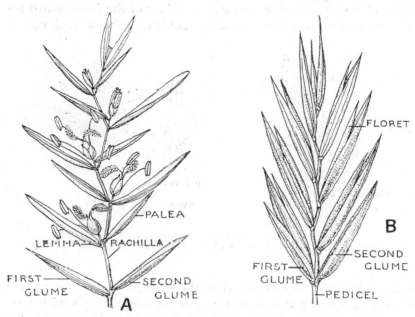

FIG. 2. The spikelets of grasses. A,diagrammatic sketch showing the general structure of a spikelet with several flowers; B, generalized spikelet, as in Brome Grass, to show the more common appearance of such structures *(from Pool, after Chase)*.

well-known value of the grasses in the natural reduction or prevention and control of erosion. Man has learned to utilize this natural behavior of certain grasses in his efforts to check the devastating effects of erosion and floods and to reclaim lands that have been at the mercy of wind and wave or of the unwise management by man for a long time.

The aerial shoots of grasses are usually cylindrical and conspicuously jointed, and the segments between the joints (internodes) are commonly hollow at maturity. Examples of important grasses in which the entire mature stem is solid (not hollow at any spot) are Indian Corn, *Zea mays,* and Sugar Cane, *Saccharum officinarum.*

The leaves of grasses are more or less ribbon-like (*linear*) and they are attached to the joints of the stem alternately in such a manner as to produce two opposite longitudinal series or *ranks* (Fig. 1). The main part of the leaf, the *blade,* is parallel-veined. The basal portion of each leaf more or less completely surrounds the stem, thus forming a *sheath* which is usually longitudinally open on the side opposite to the blade. The leaves of grasses grow in length because of the activity of a short growing zone *near the base* of the *blade* which remains active for a considerable time. This explains why, though a

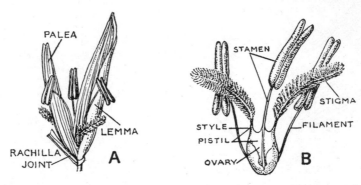

Fig. 3. A diagram to show: A, single floret of a grass with the usual parts; and B, the pistil and stamens of a single grass floret (*from Pool, after Chase*).

grazing animal may nip away most of the leaves, or a lawn mower may cut them back, in a few days the leaves are as long as they were before. Many details involving the structure of the stems and leaves are very useful in the technical delineation of the various species of grasses.

The individual flowers (Figs. 2, 3, 4) of most species of grasses are so small that they easily escape the notice of persons not unusually observing. Thus most people are surprised to learn that grasses are really flowering plants and that they produce true flowers. We commonly think of flowers as much larger structures of more or less brilliant color. Clusters of *many flowers* are, however, often obvious in the grasses. A moment's reflection will recall that the tassel of Indian corn is very prominent and well-known. That structure at the top of the corn stem is in reality a large cluster of scores of individual male or *staminate* flowers (Fig. 29). The young ear includes hundreds of female or *pistillate* flowers that are tucked away beneath the green husks. Furthermore, a close look at the flowers in the tassel when they are fresh will reveal that they are really beautifully colored. The freshly opened florets or flowers of many grasses are indeed exceedingly beautiful, but they usually "blush unseen" because they are so small that they escape notice by most human beings.

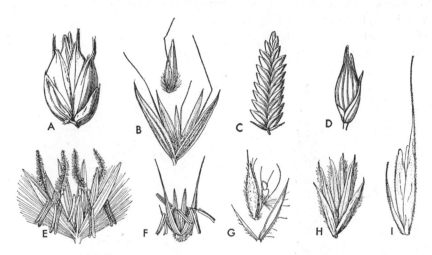

FIG. 4. The spikelets of various grasses. A, Wheat *(from Hitchcock)*; B, Oats *(from Pool, after Chase)*; C, Lovegrass *(from Hitchock)*; D, Panic Grass *(from Hitch-cock)*; E, Sugar Cane *(from Pool, after Baillon)*; F, Rye *(from Pool, after Baillon)*; G, Blue Grama *(from Pool, after Chase)*; H, Orchard Grass *(from Hitchcock)*; I, Prairie Cordgrass *(from Hitchcock)*.

The most conspicuous parts of the grass floret or flower are the more or less boat-shaped, chaffy or scale-like glumes, *bracts,* that enclose the really essential parts, that is, the stamens or *male* organs and the pistil or *female* organ (Figs. 2, 3). The pistil develops into the kernel or grain. Without these organs *no* flower really *is* a flower in the true biological sense of the word. Each flower of a grass usually includes an outer, more or less boat-shaped, veined scale known as the *lemma* or flowering *glume* and an inner or opposite, flattish scale called the *palea.* These two parts are commonly folded lengthwise, with the edges of the lemma overlapping the edges of the palea (Figs. 2, 4). Within the protective envelope thus formed are found the stamens which are usually three in number, and the single pistil with its oval or globular *ovary* and two feathery *stigmas* (Fig. 3). Flowers with this general pattern of organization are often grouped closely together on opposite sides of a zigzag axis, the *rachilla,* to form a cluster of flowers, called a *spikelet* (Figs. 2, 4). The number of flowers per spikelet varies from only one or two to several, or even twenty or more in certain species of grasses (Fig. 4). As a rule, the spikelet is subtended at the base by a pair of empty scales or *glumes,* that is, scales that lack the stamens and pistil.

Flowers and spikelets thus constituted are developed by all grasses, and in such great variety of detail as to furnish a very helpful series of structures upon which the technical classification of grasses is largely based. The number of flowers in the spikelet, the form, size, venation,

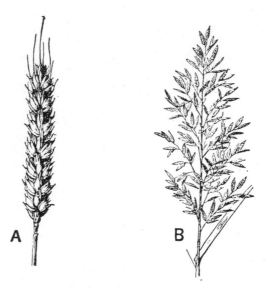

FIG. 5. The two common types of spikelet clusters or inflorescences. A, the spike, as in Wheat; B, the panicle, as in Lovegrass *(from Hitchcock).*

and surface characteristics of the lemma and palea are effectively utilized in the development of a unique scheme of classification. Among the most prominent structures of this sort are the *awns* or beards, that are developed by the extension or prolongation of the mid-vein of the lemmas. These beards are especially familiar in *bearded* wheat, as opposed to *smooth* wheat. The detailed features of the spikelet are so small in many species of the grasses that it is necessary to use a magnifier or dissecting microscope in order to make out their nature, and so to be sure of the identity of the numerous genera and species. For this reason relatively few persons have the patience or the time required to determine the identity of grasses.

The spikelets of grasses are most commonly borne singly and at the tips of numerous long and slender fibrous branches of a more or less bushy and open flower cluster known as a *panicle* (Fig. 5). Common Bluegrass, *Poa pratensis,* Brome Grass, *Bromus inermis,* and Switch Grass, *Panicum virgatum,* are good examples of grasses with this kind of clusters of spikelets. In other species the spikelets are stalkless (sessile) and more or less overlapping and closely pressed together on a congested axis (rachis) forming two overlapping series in a single, unbranched cluster known as a *spike* (Fig. 5) or "head." Wheat, *Triticum vulgare,* Rye, *Secale cereale,* and Barley, *Hordeum vulgare,* are good examples of grasses with the latter type of infloresence. The spikelets of nearly all of the grasses are formed in either panicles or spikes. Indian corn produces many female or pistillate spikelets in two-flowered pairs on the axis of the young cob or ear. If all these or half of them develop kernels we have the familiar ear of corn with its ripe kernels in rows and always in an even number of rows.

It should be emphasized at this point that the grain or kernel (i.e. the *fruit*) of grasses is produced as a result of the growth and transformation of the ovary of a single grass floret, following the fertilization of the *egg* that was formed within the tissues of the ovary. The ovary is, therefore, in all essentials the female organ of the grass. Every kernel of wheat, corn, or rice is the product of this complicated work of single grass flowers. The eggs inside the ovaries are fertilized by *sperms* that are produced by the pollen grains that in turn are formed within the anthers of the stamens. The latter, therefore, are in all essentials the male organs of the grass. Pollen grains are produced in enormous numbers by the grasses. It is said that a single plant of maize or Indian corn produces about 50,000,000 pollen grains. One has but to walk through a cornfield at the time of pollination to be impressed by the enormous quantity of the dusty, yellow pollen. This is significant in view of the fact that grasses are usually wind-pollinated. The feathery or bushy stigmas of the female organ appear to be clearly adapted to this situation, since they present a perfect catchment structure for the pollen grains. There are one thousand or more pistillate flowers or ovaries on the young cob of corn, and so if all develop, there will be about the same number of kernels on the cob at maturity.

To appreciate more fully the significant features of the biology and life history of grasses it should also be understood that most grasses produce both stamens and pistils in the same spikelet and even in the same flower. This is true in most wild species as well as in many of the cultivated grasses or cereals such as wheat, barley, oats, rye, rice. The situation in regard to this point is quite different, however, in maize or Indian corn. In that famous American grass the stamens are usually restricted to the tassel, and the pistils to the ear, but both types are borne on the same individual corn plant.

The grasses exhibit a surprising range of form and size, as well as myriads of anatomical variations that are associated with the structure of their vegetative bodies and flowers. Certain species that grow in the cold soil of the bleak wastes of arctic and alpine tundra or in the searing sun of rubble deserts may develop aerial shoots that are but an inch in height. Others that live in the perpetual favor of the humid climate of the tropical doldrums become veritable trees. The sturdy culms of certain species of bamboo that are native to Malaya are reported to reach heights of one hundred or more feet. When such plants grow in close stands they form what may be properly termed a *grass forest*. Between such extremes fall the larger number of genera and species of grasses that we find in the prairies, steppes, pampas, llanos, savannas, open ranges, meadows, pastures, and the cultivated fields, lawns, and gardens of the world.

Because of the small size and generally inconspicuous nature of the flowers of the common grasses one often notes surprise when their flowering habits are mentioned. Nevertheless, one often sees ornamental grasses of prominence and striking beauty, especially in regions that are characterized by tropical or sub-tropical climates. Clusters of the great fluffy plumes of the so-called Pampas Grass, *Cortaderia selloana,* present a crown of spectacular beauty for a flower bed or border composed of this large grass. The delicate Eulalia, *Miscanthus sinensis* (Fig. 77), and the Fountain Grass, *Pennisetum rupelii,* are likewise prized for the ornamental value of their less massive but impressive clusters of flowers. Massed individuals or even single plants of Sugar Cane, *Saccharum officinarum* (Fig. 50) are also beautiful when in bloom because of their large, vari-colored terminal panicles. One who is accustomed to discover and enjoy beauty in smaller, less grandiose "doses" is regularly thrilled by the unique aspects of the flowers of almost every kind of grass. At no season of the year are prairies ever drab, uninteresting, and monotonous wastes to a naturalist of this type.

WHERE GRASSES GROW

The distribution of grasses in time and space is notable. Fossilized remnants of their parts have been found in the rocks of Tertiary time. These unquestioned vestiges clearly indicate that grasses similar to those now gracing our prairies lived from ten to twenty million years ago. It is even probable that extensive areas of the earth were dominated by such plants during that geological period.

Grasses are found today in every condition of climate and soil from the continually warm and moist belt of equatorial calms, poleward across the intermediate latitudes to far into the arctic and antarctic regions of empty wastes and perpetual cold. They are seen at the edges of the sea and on the slopes and even the tops of mighty mountains that rear their summits to thousands of feet above sea level. Certain species are truly aquatic, whereas others seem to be found only in the precarious sites of the world's most extreme deserts. Some of them are noted as great trees in the humid tropical forests, while others are tiny dwarfs under the glaring light and the erosive brushes of the desiccating winds of hamada and dune. There are grasses that demand the sweet, well-watered and mellow soil of the meadow or lawn. Others thrive surprisingly well in the tough, soggy soil of alkaline deserts that may be so heavily laden with minerals that they crystallize to form a layer of salts on the surface over wide, glaring expanses. Wavy expanses of natural grasslands or grain fields or small fields of golden grain portray the most vivid efforts of man to utilize the grasses in his agricultural pursuits. In short, one who knows and enjoys grasses, may find some of these familiar, physiologically versatile and ubiquitous friends wherever he may travel on the land surface of the globe.

Grasses constitute the dominating feature of the landscape of some of the great types of natural vegetation that cover huge expanses in all of the world's major land areas (Fig. 6). The natural plant life of the land may be almost entirely assigned to the forests, the grasslands, the deserts, or to some of the more or less clearly defined mixtures or variations of these three basic types of vegetation. Deserts commonly include the notable presence of numerous grasses along with stunted trees or shrubs and cactuses to complete the scanty native vegetation of such places.

CHAPTER 2

The Principal Grasslands of the World

A LARGE PROPORTION, POSSIBLY MORE THAN THIRTY PER CENT OF THE land vegetation of the globe, is dominated by grasses or may, at least, be classified as potential grassland. The most of this enormous area is included in several fairly well-defined regions on the various continents. The location of these major grasslands may be shown very generally and roughly on a map, as in Figure 6. There are numerous and locally important areas of grassland of smaller size to be found on all of the continents.

Botanists and other scientists have attempted to delimit and describe the several kinds or types of natural grassland as they are more or less clearly developed in the different parts of the world. These types of vegetation are so varied and so widely spread over the continents and have been studied by so many persons who represent so many differences in training and points of view that the comparison and interpretation of the work done is difficult and uncertain.

The terminology that has been used in describing the grasslands is also variable and often confusing. Thus we find that grassland vegetation has been described as prairie, steppe, desert steppe, desert grass, orchard steppe, pampa, llano, campo, true savanna, low-grass savanna, tall-grass savanna, tree savanna, tall-grass prairie, mid-grass prairie, short-grass prairie, low prairie, high prairie, veldt, high veldt, low veldt, arctic meadow, alpine grassland, and numerous combinations and variations of these and other expressions. Many of them represent merely transitional types or complex developmental stages in the complete history of the vegetation of a given area. The same or similar terms have been used in different senses by workers in different countries, resulting in much confusion.

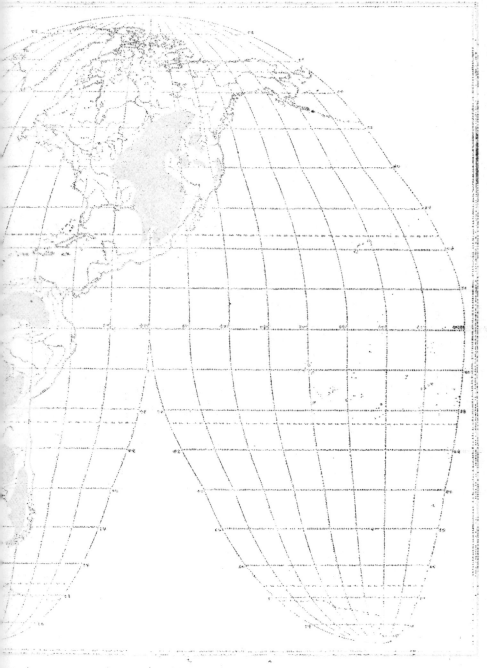

The general treatment of this subject which we present herewith must naturally overlook many of the details that reside in the climates and soils, the flora and structure of the vegetative cover of the grasslands. A student of the intimate biological relations involved would welcome and properly demand consideration of these details in a more technical analysis. For purposes of the present study we have endeavored to treat the various types of grassland simply as savannas, prairies, and steppes.

Typical savannas are extensive natural landscapes dominated by rather high, coarse grasses that seldom form turf, dotted with more or less widely scattered low trees, either as individuals or in small groups. The number, size, and form of the trees and height of the grasses vary greatly in different places, and lend distinguishing features to the various kinds of savanna. This form of grassland is most commonly found under the influence of a tropical or subtropical climate, furthermore characterized by at least a short dry season. Good examples of savannas are seen in the llano of Venezuela, the campo of Brazil, the high-grass and the tall-grass savannas of Africa.

Steppes are broad, natural, treeless landscapes that are characterized by low relief, usually developed in a semiarid or arid, warm or cool climate, and dominated by sod-forming or tufted tall-grass or short-grass vegetation (Figs. 7, 8, 9, 10, 11, 12). The warm dry season and the cold season as well may be long and severe on the steppe. Fine examples of steppes are found on the Great Plains of the United States just east of the Rocky Mountains and in the southern Russian Soviets.

Prairies are treeless, natural grasslands of low relief that are climatically and vegetationally more or less intermediate between savannas and short-grass steppes. They are less humid than savannas and less arid than steppes. They are developed in warm or cool climates, but usually are not found under tropical or subtropical climates. Prairies are furthermore characterized by deep, dark, fertile soils that are covered with sod-forming, tall grasses. The world's classic examples of prairie are found in the Trans-Mississippi Valley, the great Black Earth Belt of Russia, especially in Ukrainia, and the more humid pampa of Argentina. Prairies and steppes were evolved and are naturally maintained by the same climatic, biological, and soil conditions under which the world's greatest wheat, corn, and cattle farms have been developed.

We have included under the areas treated as savannas many of the various kinds or types of high-grass vegetation that lie mostly within the humid tropical and subtropical climates where there is at least a short dry season. Savannas often grade into forests as the dry season becomes less distinct and into steppes or deserts as aridity increases. We have included under prairies various types of natural grassland that lie mostly within the more or less humid intermediate climates, and that have been described as prairies, tall-grass prairies, and tall-grass pampas. Steppes are natural grasslands of the semiarid and arid climates and they are largely dominated by short grasses. They often grade into true deserts in many places as the climate becomes more arid and into prairies or savannas as the climate becomes more humid.

Our treatment omits practically all consideration of the desert savannas and desert grasslands, as they are described by various authors, as well as the special grassy areas of mountains and tundra, some of which are very extensive. We have merely endeavored to present a continuous introductory view of the nature and composition of the vegetation of the world's major grassland areas. The general reader and student finds it impossible to locate such information in the available literature in English unless he has access to a great variety of widely scattered sources.

GRASSLANDS OF AFRICA

A glance at the map, Figure 6, will indicate at once that grassland is developed over an extremely large proportion of the continent of Africa. According to Shantz,[1] there are several different types of grassland represented in Africa. All of these cover one-fifth or more of the total area of the African continent. Grasses also constitute an important feature of the flora of certain other areas of Africa, especially those that are more properly classified as deserts, dry woodland, and mountains, which we have excluded from this treatment. The grasslands with which we are concerned here, and which are roughly included in the map of Africa, may be briefly described under the general terms of savanna and prairie.

The vast African savannas are most widely represented by two quite different types of grassland namely, the high-grass savanna (high-grass-low tree) and the tall-grass savanna (Acacia-tall grass). The former closely hugs the tropical rain forest which is centered in the Congo basin of equatorial Africa. The latter type of savanna lies

---

[1] The best description of the grasslands of Africa is found in "The Vegetation and Soils of Africa," by H. L. Shantz and C. F. Marbut, published jointly by the National Research Council and the American Geographical Society in 1923.

outward or beyond the poleward borders of the high-grass savanna, and in the eastern and southern parts of the continent. The distinct distribution of these two kinds of grassland is not differentiated on the map; no attempt has been made to show each by separate symbols.

The high-grass savanna, with its grasses reaching heights of 10 to 12 feet, and its low trees distributed singly or in groups, begins on the west coast of the continent above Dakar at about 15° North latitude. It extends southward from that point until it meets the northern front of the tropical rain forest of Liberia and the Ivory coast at about 8° North latitude. From this, the western flank, this warm, sprawling, central African savanna sweeps eastward as a broad zone of grassland nearly across the continent. It is essentially continuous with the southern Sudan. This belt narrows somewhat as the valley of the Nile is reached, but it does not extend to the Ethiopian highlands. A broad lobe of this same type of savanna is found in west Africa south of the equatorial rain forest. It stretches eastward along the tenth parallel, below the southern border of the rain forest to near the shore of Lake Tanganyika. This lobe of high-grass savanna, along with broad strips of the tall-grass savanna to the south and east, practically encloses Bechuanaland and Northern Rhodesia.

The most widely distributed type of African grassland is the tall-grass savanna. This type, with grasses 3 to 5 feet tall, and scattered trees, lies poleward from the broad belt of the above high-grass savanna north of the equator. This belt of grassland begins on the west coast above the latter type and runs eastward as a continuous belt across the northern Sudan, becoming somewhat broader as the highlands of Ethiopia are reached and surrounded. It marches southward from the latter center across Uganda, and Kenya, to the east of Lake Victoria, and on southward near the east coast and across Tanganyika, Southern Rhodesia, the Transvaal, Orange Free State, and Natal. From there it cuts westward and northward across the northern Kalahari and on to the west where it is seen as a prominent belt near the west coast and continues northward where it meets the great lobe of high-grass savanna in Angola or Portuguese West Africa. No attempt has been made to show the distinctly different distribution of these two types of grassland on our map. They are run together as one broad and continuous belt. The tall-grass savanna was once very famous for its herds of wild game animals that grazed on the native forage grasses.

These tremendous expanses of grassland would be enlarged even more widely both to the north and south of the equator if we were to include within the savannas certain arid "forest savannas" and desert grassland types in which grasses are more or less well represented. The vast, dry forest region of northern Rhodesia and Portuguese West Africa, for instance, has been included in the African savanna by certain writers.

A third, but much smaller type of African grassland worthy of mention is represented by the tall-grass (high veldt) prairies of the Transvaal and Orange Free State. Prominent areas of this type lie within or are more or less surrounded by the dry tall-grass savanna of the preceding paragraphs. This type is not specially indicated on the map, but is included, without demarcation along with the high-grass and tall-grass savannas, in the vast expanses of the African grassland. These tall-grass prairie areas of the Transvaal are developed under a temperate climate, and the soils are generally dark-colored, deep and fertile, much as in the tall-grass prairies of North America. This is a notably rich agricultural section of South Africa, important for sheep and cattle grazing and corn and sorghum production.

Many genera and species of grasses of great diversity are represented in the immense African grasslands. The type of humid high-grass savanna that most closely bounds the tropical rain forest includes species of Bluestem Grasses, such as *Andropogon schimperi,* Jaragua Grass, *Hyparrhenia rufa,* also Bentham Grass, *Pennisetum benthami,* Cogon Grass, *Imperata cylindrica,* and Elephant Grass, *Pennisetum purpureum.* Many cultivated grasses such as the sorghums, millets, and rice are grown by the natives within these humid natural grasslands.

The grasses that characterize the somewhat less humid tall-grass savanna are not so high, but tend to be from 3 to 5 feet tall and to form continuous stands, through which there are scattered groups of low, bushy trees or single trees, largely acacias. These grasses belong to such genera as *Andropogon, Hyparrhenia,* and *Themeda,* and they produce excellent forage for grazing animals, especially during the rainy season. Many of the common varieties of cultivated sorghums probably originated in this belt.

Where the environment becomes more arid and desert conditions tend to be extreme, as especially toward the Sahara, the African grasslands are characterized by numerous grasses of lower stature and scattered distribution. These include various species of Wire Grasses, such as *Aristida hordeacea, A. congesta, A. pungens,* Rhodes Grass,

Chloris gayana, Natal Grass, *Tricholena rosea,* Woolly Finger Grass, *Digitaria eriantha,* and many others.

The grasses in the red soils of the Transvaal and the Orange Free State prairies include Rooi Grass, *Themeda triandra,* Lovegrass, *Eragrostis brizoides,* the Bluestems, *Andropogon amplectens, A. hirtiflorus,* and *Hyparrhenia hirta.* The areas dominated by these grasses rather closely resemble the bluestem prairies of North America. The cultivated crops of this valuable agricultural region are also much like those of our American prairies, and they include corn, sorghums, alfalfa, potatoes, and a variety of fruits.

GRASSLANDS OF SOUTH AMERICA

The natural grasslands of the South American continent are best developed in three fairly well-defined and separate regions. These are the alternately wet and semiarid llano or savanna of the Orinoco basin, mostly in Venezuela and the Guianas, the vast, deeply lobed campo or savanna of the uplands of central and southeastern Brazil, and the pampa or prairie and related types of Uruguay and the sprawling Argentine. The general outlines of these regions are roughly shown on the map (Fig. 6). A glance at them will reveal how enormous the combined area is. About one-third of the total area of the continent, or approximately 2,200,000 square miles, is included in these three grassy regions.

The main South American grasslands are developed under three very different climatic conditions. The Venezuelan section and the major Brazilian sections are included in the tropical savanna type of climate. The grasslands of Uruguay and extreme southern Brazil are included in the humid subtropical climate. The pampa and arid grasslands of Argentina are features of somewhat less humid and steppe types of climate. This climatic grouping seems to indicate that the three areas reveal not only different climatic conditions but also a great difference in their vegetational features.

The llano of Venezuela and campo of Brazil represent a variety of savanna types that lie far enough north and south of the equator to be influenced by the respective belts of trade winds. The dry period extends from two to six months during the low-sun season. The lower lands in the sparsely populated llano of the Orinoco basin are wet and often flooded from April to October, but from November to April the same areas dry out to a degree almost approaching desert conditions.

Great areas that are characterized by the presence of tall and low bunch grasses are seen in the Venezuelan and Guianan llanos. Such species as Bluestem, *Andropogon condensatus,* Oil Grass, *Cymbopogon rufus,* Dropseed, *Sporobolus indicus,* Crinkle-Awn, *Trachypogon plumosus,* and Guinea Grass, *Panicum maximum,* may be mentioned. The latter species covers vast but broken and more or less interrupted areas of plains with a growth that becomes four to five feet tall. The high-grass savanna near the streams is often characterized by the presence of Elephant Grass, *Paspalum purpureum.* Many other grasses are seen in various parts of the llanos, including such species as *Aristida riparia, A. cognatum, Paspalum contractum, Andropogon angustatus, A. selbanus,* and *Sporobolus cubensis.*

The extensive Brazilian campo, with its dominant park-like grassland, also experiences an alternation of extremely wet and extremely dry periods. The rainy months are December to March. The driest period is in June, July, and August. The vegetation of these areas is characterized by widespread expanses of tall, coarse grasses, without sod-forming tendencies. Among these are Molasses Grass, *Melinis minutiflora,* Guinea Grass, *Panicum maximum,* Jaragua Grass, *Hyparrhenia rufa,* and Para Grass, *Panicum purpurascens.* These areas often show single individuals and scattered clumps of low trees and shrubs. The proportion of trees in the mixture varies greatly from places where they are quite dominant, with little grass, to where they are seldom seen over wide stretches of treeless plains. Trees sometimes develop so luxuriantly along the larger streams of the type that dense jungles are formed, thus resembling the vegetation over wide areas in the southern Sudan. Grazing is the principal activity of the campo, but the quality of the livestock is rather low. Improved breeds of livestock and better management of stock and pastures would greatly increase returns to the owners.

The middle and high latitude grasslands of Argentina lie within very different climatic conditions and naturally, therefore, they show many striking biological differences as compared with the more northerly South American areas. In general, this subhumid to semiarid and arid region embraces broad level plains and plateaus with extensive north and south elongation which are continuous from the eastern foothills of the Andes to the Atlantic. This vast area as a whole is about six hundred miles wide in its broad north-central portion. It extends from the Gran Chaco of Argentina astride the Tropic of Capricorn in the north to southern Patagonia and to the tip of Tierra del Fuego in the south, at about 55°, a distance of 2,500 miles or more.

The broad plain of the main northern body of this great grassland region of Argentina gradually tapers southward as a narrowing belt over the tableland of Patagonia until it stretches nearly to the tip of the continent. This long southern extension of the region is arid to subhumid, the precipitation ranging from less than six inches toward the Andes to thirty or more inches toward the seaboard. The scanty rainfall toward the west is reflected in the sparse vegetation which consists of a more or less broken cover of short grasses (steppe) and this is marked in the more arid situations by low tufted shrubs, and the scattered mats of perennial herbs. This is the *monte,* or the extremely arid, steppe-like or desert grassland.

Eastward, beyond the *monte* to the Atlantic, in the north central portion of this far-flung country and more or less radiating from the mouth of the Plate river, is a broad, more humid or transition region of low relief with deep, dark soils. There, under the more favorable conditions, the grasses are of the taller, sod-forming species. Trees are almost entirely absent, however, except along the few stream courses. The vegetation is much like that of the prairies of North America and the more northern or less arid steppe lands of Russia. This is the *real pampa* as the Argentinian thinks of it. The common practice outside South America of applying the term "pampas" to the grasslands of Argentina in general or in their entirety should be abandoned. The pampa in this restricted true sense extends from the Atlantic shore westward for about 400 miles and north and south about 700 miles. This flat region of more than 250,000 square miles is furthermore characterized by its deep, dark, loess soil. It includes nearly one-fourth the area of the Argentine Republic. This is the nation's most valuable agricultural district, wherein most of the wheat, corn, and other crops especially flax and alfalfa are produced, and where the great herds of improved cattle are notable features. The more or less similar adjacent region of Uruguay is also ideally adapted to cattle and sheep ranching. The natural forage of the pampa is widely supplemented by extensive pastures of brome grass and alfalfa.

The pampa in this true sense, is in its typical expression generally occupied by two common types of grasses. These are the *pasto duro,* or tall, rather hard, but nutritious species of grasses that are suitable for horses and cattle, and the *pasto blando,* or shorter species that are good for cattle and sheep. A large proportion of the beef cattle of Argentina is produced upon enormous ranches of the pampa or *estan-*

cias, as they are called. These are private lands which include from
5,000 acres to 80,000 acres under a centralized management, but often
with many smaller units under sublease operation.

There are more than three hundred species of grasses to be found
on the Argentinian pampa. The various types of grasses which are
most abundant over the great *estancias* and which usually give distinction to the region as a whole include numerous species of Needle
Grass, *Stipa,* such as *S. neesiana,* Bluegrass, *Poa,* Dropseed Grass, *Sporobolus indicus,* Brome Grasses, *Bromus,* such as Cebadilla, *B. unioloides,*
and Rescue Grass, *B. catharticus,* Gamilla, *Paspalum notatum,* Dallas
Grass, *P. dilatatum,* Bluestem, *Andropogon, A. saccharoides,* Millet
Grass, *Panicum,* Triple-Awn Grass, *Aristida,* Wild Barley, *Hordeum,*
Melic Grass, *Melica,* Candy Grass, *Eragrostis,* Quake Grass, *Briza, B.
triloba,* and Carpet Grass, *Axonopus compressus.* Students of North
American grasses will recognize these familiar genera, many species of
which are abundantly represented in our own grasslands. The so-
called "pampas grass," of fine ornamental value, *Cortaderia selloana,*
is characteristic of the more humid portions of the pampa, and is of
value solely as an ornamental.

Overgrazing and other features of poor soil management have resulted in severe soil deterioration and wind erosion on some of the
ranches of the Argentine. The government has attempted to control
these conditions by planting Marram Grass, *Ammophila arenaria,* on
the dunes and sandy soils.

The extensive arid steppes of Patagonia stretch southward from
the above pampa to the straits of Magellan and beyond to the tip of
Tierra del Fuego. Such lands are characterized by scanty vegetation
in which low shrubs, grasses, and mat-like growths are often prominent.
Livestock growing is the principal industry there, especially wool
sheep and goats. Much of the land is included in huge *estancias,* some
of them of as much as 60,000 acres, with as many as 125,000 head of
sheep. Large freezing installations known as *frigerificos* are found as
far south as the Straits of Magellan. Lamb and mutton from those
processing plants are sent to the European markets.

The natural pastures of Patagonia are much more barren and cold
than those of the pampa. There are many alkaline lakes scattered
through the area. Patagonia and the pampa combined include nearly
the whole of Argentina east of the foothills of the Andes except for
the narrow belt of arid lands along the Andes mountain front (the
monte) where the scanty vegetation supports herds of sheep and goats.

GRASSLANDS OF NORTH AMERICA

The varied prairies and steppes of the deep interior of North America cover a far-flung expanse of plain and rolling territory which is centered about the 100th meridian and extends from 20° North latitude to about 54° North latitude (Fig. 6). Thus it stretches northward from the arid plateau of northern Mexico entirely across the United States to southeastern British Columbia, the flat expanses of

FIG. 7. Big Bluestem, a characteristic member of the flora of the North American tall-grass prairie *(from Hitchcock)*.

FIG. 8. Little Bluestem, an important member of the prairie flora of North America *(from Hitchcock)*.

Alberta, Saskatchewan and southwestern Manitoba, and from the Gulf coast of Texas to eastern Oklahoma, central Missouri, northern Illinois, southern and western Minnesota and thence to the Rocky Mountains. Besides this vast main body of prairie there are other outlying grasslands of importance that are interrupted by the mountains farther westward, as in New Mexico and Arizona, southwestern Wyoming, northern Utah, southern Idaho, southeastern Oregon, and northern Nevada. Other more or less distinct areas of natural grasslands lie in southeastern Washington, on the Columbia plateau, and in the great interior valley of California between the Sierra Nevada and the Coast ranges.

Climatically, the continuous main component of our North American prairies varies from subhumid along the eastern border to semi-arid and arid toward the western limits. This represents a range of rainfall from 35 inches in the east to 10 inches or less in certain districts of the far west and south.

FIG. 9.   Porcupine Grass, or Needle Grass, commonly seen with the bluestems *(from Hitchcock).*

FIG. 10.   Buffalo Grass, one of the most famous and valuable of all American grasses *(from Hitchock).*

Koeppen and Geiger's popular scheme of classification of the world's climate includes portions of this vast North American prairie area in five different climatic types. The southern part of the eastern half in the United States lies within the short-cold-winter, long-hot-summer form of the intermediate climates; the northern part of the eastern half within the long-cold-winter, short-hot-summer type of intermediate climate; the western half of the main body, commonly known as the "Great Plains," lies in the middle-latitude-steppe type of

climate.   The interior valley prairie of California is included in the
dry subtropical type of climate.

The above classification suggests that one would probably find
different types or associations of grassland species in various portions
of the region, as is notably true.   However, the true nature of the
vegetation is usually revealed by the presence and dominance of either
tall grasses, mid grasses, short grasses, bunch grasses, or by various mix-

Fig. 11.   Blue Grama, a common associate
of Buffalo Grass on the North American
prairies *(from Hitchcock).*

Fig. 12.   Indian Grass, an important
member of the tall-grass flora of
the North American prairies
(from Hitchcock).

tures of these four types.   Certain large areas in the more arid and
desert-like prairies (steppes) are often controlled by various species of
shrubs such as mesquite, sagebrush, catclaw, rabbitbrush, and even
cactuses.   As a rule, these latter forms owe their prominence to some
disturbing influence such as over-grazing, prolonged drought, or fire.

Botanists and livestock men have recognized several different types
of grassland associations in this region.   These are dependent upon
the presence of certain distinctive species.   The *true* prairie, for in-

stance, is recognized by the presence of certain tall species of Bluestem, *Andropogon furcatus* (Fig. 7), Dropseed Grass, *Sporobolus heterolepis,* Indian Grass, *Sorghastrum nutans* (Fig. 12), and Needle Grass, *Stipa spartea* (Fig. 9). The *coastal* prairie is distinguished by certain other species of bluestem such as *Andropogon saccharoides,* and Needle Grass, *Stipa leucotricha,* whereas the *shortgrass* prairie of the high plains is typified by the presence of Buffalo Grass, *Buchloë dactyloides* (Fig. 10), and Blue Grama Grass, *Bouteloua gracilis* (Fig. 11). The *desert* grasslands and high plains type of grasslands of the west and southwest are often characterized by the presence of bunch grasses of

Fig. 13.   Curly Mesquite, a very important species of the southwestern range
(from Hitchcock).

the Triple-Awn Grass type, *Aristida longiseta,* by Black Grama Grass, *Bouteloua eriopoda,* or Curly Mesquite, *Hilaria belangeri* (Fig. 13).

Savanna-like mixtures of low trees and shrubs and grasses are often seen along the borders of the American prairies, especially along the eastward and westward limits of the region where the transition is made to the more humid deciduous and arid montain forest respectively. The forest lands in the Rocky Mountains are very rich in grazing areas in which there are numerous valuable grasses. There are many notable similarities in the flora and general conditions between the North American prairies, the pampas of South America, and the steppes of Russia.

A broad belt along the eastern portion of the prairie region, which is characterized by deep, dark soils, and the presence of the tall-grass prairie, is largely devoted to general farming including corn and live-stock, especially cattle and swine. Toward the west and throughout much of the drier short-grass prairies (steppes) wheat production and cattle ranching are the major activities of the scantier population. The range cattle from the prairies have always played a very important part in the livestock industry of America. The cattle industry in the United States in normal times is a 5.5 to 6.0 billion-dollar business, exceeding in value even steel and automobiles. The vast wheat fields that extend north and south across this area are the most notable examples of the adaptation of cultivated crops to the American grass-lands.

GRASSLANDS OF THE SOVIET REPUBLIC

We may group the major grassland areas of the Soviet Union under the one general term of *steppes*. One should recall, however, that there has been considerable variation in the definition and application of this word by climatologists, biologists, and pedologists. More gen-erally, the term has been applied to the semiarid areas that are more or less dominated by short grasses, and that lie between the tall-grass types of true prairie or pampa and the distinctly arid and even desert types of vegetation. The steppe in this sense is in reality a transition from one of these types of grassland to the other. As an illustration of this usage we may cite the area within the North American grass-lands that is often designated as the short-grass plains.

For purposes of this brief summary the term steppe is used to cover, in a broad sense, all of the variations of the grassland types that occur in Russia and the neighboring regions except those of the tundra and the desert. It has long been known that the Russian steppes have much in common with the prairie of North America and the pampa of Argentina when these two terms are used in the broadest sense. Notable similarities are found in the general climatic features, the soils, the native flora, and natural vegetation, as well as the general agricultural activities of the three widely separated regions. At this point we may mention the area of grassland which is centered on the plains of Hungary, as shown in Figure 6. These Hungarian steppes, or *pusztas,* are much like the steppes of southwestern and western Russia.

The main body of the Russian steppes marches northward and eastward for hundreds of miles from the region of the lower Dnieper, Black Sea, Caucasus and the North Caspian basin (Kazakh) over a far-reaching expanse of territory to the east. On the north and toward the west this vast area meets the southern border of the oak and beech forests (the woodland steppe) and farther eastward the more northerly coniferous forest (taiga) regions of middle and far eastern Siberia. The winters are long and cold, the summers relatively short and cool. To the south of the Siberian forests the steppes extend across the huge Kazakh Republic with its arid types, and onward to the desert lands of the huge Kirghiz Republic, and other lands in the interior of central and eastern Asia. The general trend of the region as a whole is eastward on both sides of the parallel of 50° North latitude. This is in marked contrast with the main body of the North American prairies which extend generally *north* and *south* on both sides of the meridian of 100° West longitude. The general distribution and extent of this huge and significant region of the Soviets are indicated on the accompanying map (Fig. 6).

The more striking and typical aspects of this enormous area toward the west and north are revealed in the relatively flat or undulating, treeless plain at low altitude and low relief. This far-flung expanse is the natural home of a variety of tall grasses in the more humid north and west borders and of short grasses and scattered desert shrubs (desert steppe) in the arid southern and eastern stretches. The west Russian steppes are, therefore, much like the more eastern American prairies, and the southern steppes more like the western and south-western semiarid American prairies. The seeming monotony of these types is often modified on the north by the presence of extensive meadow lands and by trees of both the deciduous and evergreen forests. To the far south and east it is often broken by low trees, shrubs, and tufted grasses as it merges into the deserts and bolder outlines of the extreme south and the far eastern expressions of the widely scattered Asiatic grasslands.

The soils of the main area of the Russian steppes vary from the deep, neutral, fertile, black or brown earths of the Dnieper, Don, and Volga basins with their natural cover of tall grasses, to the sandy, shingle wastes, hard clays, and sterile alkaline soils of the arid areas farther south and east with their sparse cover of short grasses and generally very scanty flora. The black earth belt of the Russian steppes is probably the largest continuous expanse of such soil in the world.

The long summer drought that prevails over large tracts of the more southern and eastern stretches of the region are recorded in the extremely arid aspects—the Desert Steppe—that prevail throughout the area, especially as in the Caspian-Aral desert, and in the Takla Makan and Gobi far to the east.

The black earth region west of the Volga, including the Ukrainian Republic, is the most important agricultural center of the vast land that is governed by the Soviets. This is the most significant section of the "Heartland" of the European-Asiatic continent, and it is the great wheat country of the Soviets and the region of the most varied and vigorous activity of the whole nation. No wonder that it was a major objective of the Nazi armies. Strenuous and successful efforts by Russian scientists in cooperation with the government are gradually expanding the agricultural borders of this spacious land both eastward and northward. It is reported that more than 17,000,000 acres even of the virgin Siberian steppes to the east were broken up and put to crops during the Second Five-Year Plan.

The black-earth steppes, such as spread across the region west of the Volga and the Don, are characterized by many species of tall prairie grasses, among which the Thyrsa Grass, *Stipa pennata,* is one of the commonest. This grass often dominates vast stretches of the less arid steppe and deep black soil much as do the related tall grasses of the eastern portion of the North American prairies. Other species that are to be noted there arc June Grass, *Koeleria cristata,* Sheep Fescue, *Festuca ovina,* and various other species of *Stipa,* of *Poa,* the Bluegrasses, and Sweet Grasses, *Hierochloa.* June Grass is the same valuable forage species that is an important constituent of much of the native prairie pastures of the United States. The thinner and less fertile steppe lands are often marked by Thyrsa Grass also, and by other species of *Stipa,* such as *S. capillata,* which often goes under the same common name. Far to the east and south where the more arid climate of the Kirghiz prevails, occur many species of drought-enduring grasses, such as Triple-Awn Grass, *Aristida pungens,* which is also a valuable sandbinding grass.

The Asiatic portions of the Soviet steppes are broken into numerous scattered "islands" or areas with good soil but often extremely arid. They are also characterized by very severe winters. The grasses that are found there are representative of the hardiest, most drought-enduring kinds such as Crested Wheat Grass, *Agropyron cristatum,* as well as many other species of wheat grasses, Wild Rye, *Elymus* spp., and Bluejoint Grass, *Calamagrostis* spp., Needle Grass, *Stipa* spp., and Fescue, *Festuca* spp. Crested Wheat Grass has been extensively used in the United States in recent years in connection with important and successful soil conservation work on the northern Great Plains. The southeastern Soviets, northern China, and Mongolia are the home of the Goat Grasses, *Aegilops* sp., and *Haynaldia* sp., Wild Barley, *Hordeum* sp., and various species of Foxtail Grasses, *Setaria,* Fescues, *Festuca,* and Bluegrasses, *Poa.*

Other grassland areas, some of them of great extent and often widely separated, are noted in Asiatic Russia and northern China far to the east and south of the main Russian steppes. These lie in western and central Manchukuo, and south of the Great Wall in northern China, mostly to the north and west of the Whang Ho and west of its middle course. Some of these areas, especially those in the province of Ningsha, resemble the more arid Russian steppes. These grasslands are not at all well-known. In fact, their original nature has long been obscured by the changes that have accompanied the age-old activities of the human race in those lands. They are shown on the map only in a rough, tentative way. The natural vegetation of these areas varies from tall-grass prairie to the shorter, arid, bunch-grass types and scattered shrubs that dot the arid hills. There are large acreages of grain lands and livestock ranges in these areas. More scattered and less valuable features march with the hardy grasses of the tremendous arid expanses of desert, the "desert steppes," farther to the west of these lands and on into the Gobi desert.

GRASSLANDS OF AUSTRALIA

The isolated continent of Australia was the last of the world's major land areas to feel the rigorous touch of man's aggressive pioneering endeavors. Even now few people in distant lands have any real appreciation of the global significance of this sixth continent "down under." The area of Australia is slightly larger than the continental United States. Australia ranks first among the nations of the world in the production of sheep and fourth in cattle. One-third of the wool exports of the world come from that land.

A very large portion of the commonwealth is included in the great interior desert heart of the nation. That is one of the most extreme and barren of all known deserts. There are few streams there and the vegetation is extremely scanty and of very little value. The population is very sparse. Certain primitive tribes of people still inhabit portions of the desert. This vast central barrenness is surrounded, except in the extreme south and southwest, by a narrow shell of semi-arid or humid lands within which one finds large areas that are characterized by humid tropical and subtropical types of climate and the Mediterranean or dry subtropical and temperate climates with their grasslands and forests.

The thinly populated natural grasslands of Australia make up a large proportion of the circum-desert shell which surrounds the arid interior of the continent (Fig. 6). A broad strip of tropical savanna and related types of warm grassland marches in a great east-west arc above the treeless and practically grassless desert of the interior. This broad belt extends northward until it reaches another narrow arc of savanna woodland, which continues on eastward, northward, and westward to the respective coasts.

This far-flung grassy arc extends to the Indian ocean on the west, and then gives way southward across western Australia to the arid *mulga* and scrub woodland or *mallee*. The wiry vegetation of the mulga consists mainly of dwarf plants of Acacia, *Acacia,* and Porcupine Grass, *Triodia irritans*. The mallee is composed of a scattered growth of Dwarf Gum trees, *Eucalyptus,* over an open stand of dry, short grasses.

The eastern arm of this major warm grassland arc marches southeastward and southward to merge into the savanna-woodland of the east and finally into the semiarid temperate grassland section of the great southeastern region of the continent. This latter extensive region presents conditions and a flora that most nearly resemble the situation upon the semiarid North American prairies and the Russian steppes. Broad areas of saltbrush vegetation (with little grass) extend westward from these temperate grasslands to and into the central desert. The scrub woodland or *mallee* forms a fairly continuous east and west belt below the southern border of the desert from the above temperate grasslands in the east to southwestern Australia.

Very valuable wheat lands and areas of general agriculture lie within the temperate grasslands portions of this great Australian grassy arc. These are largely included in Queensland, New South Wales, and Victoria. Much good pastoral land, especially for sheep, also occurs in the temperate forest area to the east as well as in the extensive saltbrush lands to the west. The dry subtropical areas of extreme southern Australia also contain excellent wheat lands. The savannas to the far north are of little value except for livestock production. The grasses of the northern savannas show a decidely seasonal type of behavior, being alternately green and fresh or brown and dried out for periods of about six months in response to the rythmical course of the seasons. The rainy season usually begins in December and so this is a fairly luscious period for the livestock. Through the dry period, the second half of the year, the animals subsist on the natural and nutritious hay of the range.

Among the valuable species of the Australian grasslands are the Mitchell Grasses, *Astrebla pectinata, A. lappacea, A. elymoides,* and *A. squarrosa.* These grasses produce fine yields of forage and will endure the rigors of heavy grazing. The wild hay of certain of these species is especially valuable for herds of livestock on the northern and eastern ranches during the dry season. Other Australian grasses that may be listed are: Bluegrass, *Dichantheum sericeum,* Wallaby Grass, *Danthonia semi-annularis,* Kangaroo Grass, *Themeda australis,* Flinders Grass, *Iseilema membranacea,* and the Tussock Grasses, *Poa caespitosa,* and *Eulalia fulva.* Silvery Sandgrass, *Spinifex hirsuta,* and the Porcupine Grass or False Spinifex, *Triodia irritans,* are distinctive of the more arid districts and sandy desert lands. Cogon or Blady Grass, *Imperata cylindrica,* is often seen in the savannas of northern Australia. This grass is said to furnish good forage, especially when in the depauperate condition, and during periods of drought. Molasses Grass, *Melinis minutiflora,* and Guinea Grass, *Panicum maximum,* are often sown for pasture grasses in the warm savannas of the far north. Several species of annual Bromes, Fescues, Oats, and Barleys are also found in the Australian grasslands. On the whole, the vast grassy domain of Australia compares favorably in the matter of livestock production and wheat culture with the related natural grasslands of North America, South America, Russia, and Africa.

CHAPTER *3*

Wheat

DURING THE VIGOROUS DECADES OF ANCIENT ROME THAT CITY WAS
noted for the numerous and beautiful palaces, temples, arches, col-
umns, stadia, circuses, baths, and private villas that graced its seven
hills and shallow valleys. The great *Circus Maximus* lay in an open
valley, the *Vallis Murcia,* between the Palatine and the Aventine hills,
toward the southern portion of the city and near the Tiber. On a
spur of the Aventine, close by the southwestern corner of the *Circus
Maximus* (Fig. 14), and overlooking the Tiber to the west was a beautiful Grecian temple known as the *Templum Cereis,* or the Temple of
Ceres. Near by, and quite appropriately, stood the *Templum Florae,*
the Temple of Flora, the Goddess of flowers.

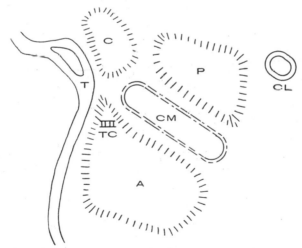

FIG. 14. Location of the Temple of Ceres, TC, in ancient Rome; A, Aventine; CM,
Circus Maximus; P, Palatine; C, Capitoline; CL, Colosseum *(from sketch made on
the spot by the author).*

Ceres was the Roman Goddess of the fields, of seed, grain and the
harvest, in short, the Goddess of Agriculture. The beautiful Ceres

29

was worshipped mostly by plebeians in the notable shrine on the hill near the great circus. The operations of the grain market were also superintended from that center. The ritual of Ceres was Greek in form and language, thus reflecting the influence of an earlier and similar deity. In fact, the temple itself was Grecian in architecture and it is said to have been built by Greek artisans. The chief festivals were celebrated in April, August and October, and were known as the *Ludi Cereis,* or the *Cerealia,* that is, the festivals of *Ceres.*

Thus we go for the source of our familiar modern word, *cereal,* to those far-off centuries and to that ancient center of human culture that was classical Rome. The word embraces much of first importance in the lives of modern men as it did in the days when Rome was the economic hub as well as the cultural center of the ancient world. The origin, development, and specialization of the words of the English tongue have since then undergone much transformation and change. The use of the word cereal was formerly extended to include beans, lentils, and other legumes, and even buckwheat and the seed of spinach, as well as the grains and the grasses themselves which produce our edible grain. The word is often expanded in modern parlance to include the more or less highly processed foods made from the grain of cereals, such as oatmeal, corn flakes, cream of wheat, grits, and the like. The tendency and the better practice now is to apply the word only to the grain or to the crop itself and to those true grasses which produce the edible grain for the use of man and other animals. Mankind continues to fashion its daily program in intimate association with these most valuable grasses. The march of modern mechanization in the western world has largely followed the development of cereal agriculture and its inseparable counterpart, livestock production. The cereals contribute an increasing volume to the mighty flow of indispensable foods across the far reaches of the globe. Nations thrive or suffer when the cereals are abundant or scarce.

THE MAJOR CEREALS

WHEAT

The most important grasses in the world for the varied interests of mankind are the major cereals, wheat, rice and corn. Glutenous dough made from the fluffy flour of the wheat kernel is the prime basis of bread supply of the modern world (Fig. 15). Rice, although still widely utilized in a simpler and more primitive manner than wheat, is the greatest single competitor of wheat in its contribution of essential foods for mankind. Corn, the cereal of greatest production in the West, easily enables man to bridge his way to that other enormous supply of quite different foods that are contributed by the flesh and milk of domesticated animals.

These three master grasses present many very interesting and significant similarities and contrasts. They were brought under cultivation by man hundreds of years ago, independently, and in three widely separated areas of the globe. The three attained unusual eminence in the long and uncertain marches of mankind, but at different times and for different reasons. Rice was the stand-by of the earliest residents of the Indo-Chino-Japanese region. Wheat was the staff of life of the Mediterranean borderlands and near-by areas, corn the most

FIG. 15. The wheat plant, showing portions of the stem, the heads of bearded and smooth wheat, and the spikelet *(from Hitchcock)*.

important crop of primitive man in the American hemisphere. Rice culture originated in, and is still most typical of, the subtropical and tropical monsoon climate of Asia, although it is more and more abundantly grown in the western world. Of the three master cereals, wheat is now the most widely grown, a fact that reflects its adaptation to a great variety of climates and soils. The great areas of corn production lie, climatically, more or less midway between these extremes, but are most typical of the cooler, relatively drier weather with cold dry winters and warm subhumid summers of the intermediate continental or interior climates. Wheat produces the accepted and most popular bread supply for hundreds of widely scattered millions of all races of men throughout the world. Rice is the food crop par excellence of teeming millions in Asia's centers of densest population. Corn contributes fabulous volumes of especially effective foods for man and for the development and the finishing-off of uncountable numbers of livestock on the ranches and the farms, especially in the newer areas as well as the older regions of the western world. And, even in our intensely motorized age, this enchanting cereal of the early Americans is still of great importance also as a food for man and his faithful draft animals.

The exact place and time of the origin and earliest cultivation of wheat are effectively hidden in the baffling uncertainties that shroud the centuries before the dawn of the recorded history of man. Kernels of wheat have been found in the crumbled homes and the tombs of people who lived scores of centuries ago. The fragmentary evidence that archaeology contributes seems to indicate that this grain has been cultivated for at least 6,000 years. It was grown in the valley of the Nile about 5,000 B.C., and along the Euphrates in 4,000 B.C. Considerable support favors the opinion that the place of origin of wheat was somewhere in the area not far from the eastern Mediterranean, as in Syria or Abyssinia or some area in the Near East. It is a noteworthy fact that the plant is well adapted to the dry Mediterranean type of climate. Wheat most probably was the most important source of carbohydrate food in those early story-lands that stretch from Mesopotamia through Asia Minor to Italy, Germany, Spain, and England, when Babylon was an important capital. Wheat has continued to supply some of the most important threads that have been firmly woven into the widening fabric of civilization from those narrow, uncertain years to the global might that now staggers the imagination of man.

As the long travail of civilization and the slow evolution of the cultivated crops go, we in the United States entered the picture only yesterday. One of the first and most necessary efforts of the colonists

at Jamestown and Plymouth was to clear the forest and to sow grain in the land thus prepared. Wheat for seeding those colonial fields was brought from England, and a little later from Holland and Sweden. The prominent leaders of those earliest colonial years left abundant records that reflect the importance of this grain as they laid the foundations of the new Republic. As the hardy settlers began their slow westward marches, they took the "staff of life" with them into the different climatic conditions and soil types that were encountered. It is interesting to note that it was about one hundred and fifty years after the establishment of the colonies in Virginia and Massachusetts before the cultivation of wheat reached California from Spain by way of the West Indies and Mexico.

Wheat has been the constant companion of western man in his marches from the relative comforts of established society toward the ever-widening horizons of the globe with all their uncertainties and hardships. Thanks to the progress of biological and industrial science, man still is struggling, but now with more certain hope of success, with the varied and increasingly complex problems that are involved in adjusting wheat to an expanding natural frontier. Important features of this up-to-the-minute search involve the effort to force wheat into service for mankind in even a broader and more varied program in the future than it has had in its multi-millenial history. It is no fanciful prediction by a "black-robed professor, sitting in his ivory tower" that wheat will continue to hold its ageless place in the upward march toward the improvement and enrichment of civilization. Mankind cries out for wheat whenever hunger becomes acute and famine threatens the stability of society or government.

The empire of modern wheat culture marches from the land of the pine to the land of the palm. Wheat is being harvested somewhere in the world in every month of the year. The outermost reaches of the wheat belt sprawl across the northern hemisphere to beyond 60° North latitude, and nearly to the Arctic circle in Alaska and Scandinavia. In the southern hemisphere it marches beyond the parallel of 40° South in Argentina and New Zealand. Even some areas of important production approach these widely separated parallels. In the other direction we may say that the sun scarcely sets on this vast dominion of wheat: it encircles the globe!

A closer scrutiny of Figure 16 reveals the more significant fact that the major wheat producing areas of the globe lie between the parallels of 30° and 55° North and between 30° and 40° South latitude. It is a notable fact that this is also the zone of the greatest and most vigorous activities of the human race. Within these two belts, north and south of the equator, one readily identifies seven major regions of wheat production, namely, southern Russia, southern Europe, northwestern India (slightly more southerly), north-central China, southeastern Australia, South America (Argentina), and central North America. The general European region may be subdivided into the Hungarian Plain, the Danube Basin, Western Europe, and the Mediterranean area. Of the North American center there are three principal subdivisions, the southern Great Plains area of the United States, the northern Great Plains area of the United States and Canada, and the Columbia Plateau area of Washington, Idaho, and Oregon. These most important areas of wheat culture in the world today may be summarized as follows:

I. THE RUSSIAN REGION (U.S.S.R.).
II. THE EUROPEAN REGION.
    1. The Plain of Hungary.
    2. The Danube Basin.
    3. Western Europe.
    4. The Mediterranean area.
III. THE NORTHWESTERN INDIA REGION.
IV. THE NORTH-CENTRAL CHINA REGION.
V. THE SOUTHEASTERN AUSTRALIA REGION.
VI. THE SOUTH AMERICAN REGION.
    1. The Pampa of Argentina.
VII. THE NORTH AMERICAN REGION.
    1. The southern Great Plains of the United States.
    2. The northern Great Plains of the United States and Canada.
    3. The Columbia Plateau area.

The annual wheat crop of the world as a whole reaches the astonishing total of about 5.2 billion bushels (Table 1). The Russian Republics (U.S.S.R.) have commonly lead all of the above areas of the great empire of wheat in acreage and production. In a recent year Soviet farmers produced about 925 million bushels of wheat on about 86 million acres. China was third in 1945 with a reported 715 million bushels. In 1945 the United States led the world with 1,123,143,000 bushels. Then, with a large drop, India 390, Canada 305, France 184, Italy 154, Argentina 149, and Germany 149 million. Yields per acre on the average are commonly greatest in Germany, 29 bushels, France 23, and Italy 21.

The heaviest producing area in Russia is in the deep, loessal, Chernozem black earth soils of the Ukraine Soviet and the Crimea, that great territory extending in general westward from the lower Volga to the Romanian frontier (Fig. 16). Winter wheat is grown across the southern portion of that area, and spring wheat in the north. Durum wheat is grown in abundance in certain of the driest areas of the Russian steppes where the climatic uncertainties are more severe. The significance of wheat and grain in general to the Soviet Union is picturesquely portrayed by the great seal of the Union and the beautiful seals of the sixteen Soviet Republics, every one of which features sheaves or heads of grain. The climates of the Asiatic Soviets are usually too severe, too dry or too cold, for the best wheat culture. But

Fig. 17. Preparing fields for wheat on a large scale with the use of power machinery, in Russia. *(Photo from Sovefoto.)*

expansion of the agricultural efforts of the Russians to the east is yielding much encouragement. The huge grain elevators of Siberia are eloquent testimony of the returns of the spring wheat crop of that land. It is reported that more than 17,000,000 acres of virgin steppe in Siberia were put into cultivation during the second Five-Year Plan. Expansion of irrigation east of the Volga and in general in the eastern Soviets has also added greatly to the area of land under cultivation. Large areas of pasture land have been freed for grain culture in Russia because of the great advances in agricultural mechanization (Fig. 17).

Farther westward in Europe we find that the plains of Hungary are ideally favored by climate and soil for wheat production. The soils of the broad basin of the Danube, across the mountains from Hungary, are likewise excellent for wheat, but the climate is not so dependable as on the Hungarian Plain. This combined area is of exceedingly great importance as a producer of foods for all of the states of central Europe. It is often called the "bread basket" of Europe.

The famous mild, humid winters and the clear, dry summers of the Mediterranean basin favor wheat culture in extreme southern Europe and across the sea in North Africa. Much wheat is grown among the ancient ruins of Spain and Italy, and on the narrow northern fringe of Africa in Algeria and Morocco.

Wheat is extensively grown under irrigation in the Punjab and in the valley of the upper Ganges of northwestern India. It is surprising, perhaps, that that area should rank fourth among all of the great wheat-growing areas, but of course, practically the entire yield is now used at home with but little left to export. The relentless nature of the monsoonal climate forces the Indian farmer to sow early varieties of wheat. But even then, if the needed rain happens to come too late, his crop may be ruined by the fatal combination of increasingly high humidity and high temperature before the crop can mature.

TABLE 1.—*The Production of Wheat (bushels) in Various Countries and the World, for 1945 except where noted otherwise.*

United States	1,123,143,000
Russia (1930–1934)	860,448,000
China (1935–1939)	715,536,000
India	390,432,000
Canada	305,912,000
France	184,000,000
Italy	154,542,000
Germany (1944)	149,913,000
Argentina	149,545,000
Australia and New Zealand	145,500,000
Romania (1935–1939)	140,816,000
Hungary (1935–1939)	91,210,000
Africa	85,000,000
United Kingdom	79,333,000
Poland (1935–1939)	77,245,000
Spain	73,000,000
Bulgaria	41,818,000
Yugoslavia	34,000,000
World, total	5,200,000,000

The picture of enormous wheat production in China presents an interesting conflict between this master cereal of the West and rice, the master of the East. Wheat, the natural product of a cool, dry or semiarid climate here comes into direct competition with rice, the cereal that is quite at home in the hot, humid climate of southern China. This situation is more or less avoided by the Chinese, however, by the restriction of wheat to the cooler, drier, northern and northeastern portions of the country. Some progress has been made in methods that permit the growth of wheat and rice even in the same locality by growing wheat during the cooler, drier period and rice during the hotter, more humid season of the monsoonal year. Thus, we see that the northerly Chinese farmers may actually produce two cereal crops in a single year by this system. Here, and in significant reality, East and West have come to meet on common ground but in very different seasons.

There are four major and rather well-defined regions of China in which wheat is an important crop. The most northerly of these is the irregular, sprawling, semiarid to arid spring wheat belt which marches westward from Jehol across the extensive plains of north China to the frontier of Sinkiang. This spacious land of wheat is a thousand miles long. It runs more or less parallel with the barren southern stretches of Mongolia and disappears in the deserts to the west. Southward from about the center of this spring wheat belt lies a large region, including lands both to the east and to the west of the Whang Ho, in which winter wheat and millet are grown. Extensive tracts of deep loess soils in the provinces of Shansi, Shensi, and Kansu are included within this important agricultural region. A third region of cereal production extends eastward from the winter wheat area across the yellow plains of Hopei, Shantung, and southeastern Jehol to the Yellow Sea. Winter wheat shares this broad area with the kaoliang sorghums. The fourth major region within which wheat is an important crop, lies immediately south from the winter wheat-kaoliang area, and mostly north of the Yangtze. The provinces of Honan, Hopei, Anhwei, and Kiangshu, the great hinterlands of Shanghai, are included in this prominent region where wheat meets and shares the honors with rice. The latter cereal rapidly becomes the dominant crop of the warmer, more humid provinces farther to the south and west.

Throughout these important, far-flung agricultural districts of China the farm population ranges from 1,000 to more than 1,200 per square mile of the area in crops. Improved varieties of grain and better methods of field management throughout these expansive wheat lands would seem to promise much greater returns in wheat to modern resurgent China. Limited irrigation is already provided in certain localities. More land might be cultivated and a larger use of irrigation water within this vast empire of wheat would go far toward the relief of the perennially underfed people of the giant struggling nation.

Wheat production in Australia and New Zealand (145,500,000 bushels in 1945) is far above the demands of the home folks. The exportation of a large proportion of the crop of her semiarid lands of the southeast and the southwest brings Australia sharply into competition with the world's larger producers. The well-known "grain race" for distant European ports between westbound steamships laden with Australian wheat and the picturesque sailing vessels also loaded with wheat, but bound eastward around Cape Horn, reflects this situation. The latter ships strive to utilize the advantage of sailing with the eastward sweep of the "roaring forties," the global belt of prevailing westerly winds that are especially powerful in that particular belt of latitude. The grain is produced in the dry, subtropical areas of New South Wales, Victoria, South Australia, and on a much smaller scale in West Australia, where the winter rains bring from 10 to 20 inches of moisture. Dry farming is practiced in the production of wheat in the more arid western districts. Since the first World War there has been an increasing demand for Australian wheat in the Far East, especially by Japan.

The story of wheat production in South America stems from the famous "wheat crescent" of Argentina (Fig. 16). This great semicircular area of the Argentine bulge radiates to the southwest for hundreds of miles from the vast waters of the Rio de la Plata, or Plate river. This main area of wheat lands is essentially a broad arc which is more than six hundred miles long and embraces the northern, western and southern reaches of the Argentinian pampa. It extends northward from southern Buenos Aires province to northern Cordoba and central Santa Fe. This immense sweep of wheat lands lies at about the same latitude south as do Kansas, Oklahoma, and northern Texas in the north. Extensive arid lands lie to the west of the wheat crescent, but to the east the increasingly humid climate serves to establish the famous *estancias* with their noteworthy crops of corn, flax and pasture.

The climate of that region is less tropical than that in far northern Argentina, in fact it is usually classified as humid subtropical. This is somewhat like the climate of southeastern United States, but the precipitation and humidity of the latter region is higher than in the wheat-growing area of the Argentine. The climate becomes drier and drier as one goes farther into the central interior and western part of the country. There are wide variations in rainfall and temperature within the wheat crescent. The soils of this great and growing wheat land are deep, black, and fertile, in fact very much like the rich soils of the tall-grass prairie of middle western United States and Ukraine. The near-black upper soil of the pampa is about two feet deep and this lies upon a brownish subsoil about six feet deep. Enormous expanses of the original native grassland of the pampa have been broken up and put to wheat and alfalfa, and cattle production is a dominant activity in many parts of the area.

Because of the relatively low population Argentina exports a large proportion of her wheat. In this matter she is second only to Canada. The fact that harvest time in Argentina is during late November, December, and January, when stocks of wheat in foreign countries of the northern hemisphere are becoming depleted, favors her export relationships. Argentina could probably increase her production of wheat to a considerable degree. At present, wheat culture is already replacing grazing in certain areas. The acreage in 1945 was about 10,030,000, the most of which was included in large private estates or *estancias* of 10,000 to 30,000 acres, much of which is leased to farmers in smaller units.

The wheat "empire" of North America is a tremendous one (Figs. 16 and 18). As in South America, our wheat-producing region is closely correlated with the deep, dark soil of our natural grasslands, but of the middle interior of the continent, and far from coastal ports. This region marches over the prairies and plains that extend from northern Texas to the Peace river district of northern Alberta, a distance of about 2,000 miles. Kansas commonly leads in wheat production within this area (Table 2). This area in fact begins close to the long, hot, and dry subtropical climate of the south and ends in the north close to the short, cold summers of the subpolar climate. The western border parallels more or less the arid foothills of the Rocky Mountains. The eastern limits merge into the western fringes of the cotton belt, the corn belt, and the dairy pasture lands still farther northward. This enormous domain is conveniently divided into the southern Great

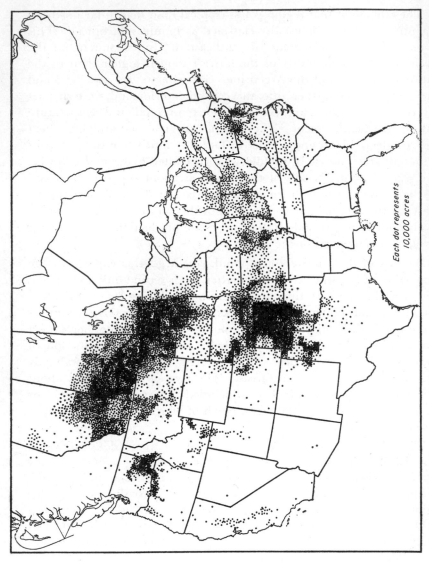

Each dot represents
10,000 acres

Fig. 18. Location and acreage of wheat in the United States and Canada, from the 1929 and 1930 census respectively. The acreage is probably somewhat greater at the present time. (*Photo from Bureau of Plant Industry, Division of Cereal Crops and Diseases, U. S. Department of Agriculture.*)

TABLE 2.—*The Production of Wheat (bushels) in Various States for 1945.*

Kansas	207,961,000
North Dakota	161,888,000
Nebraska	85,212,000
Oklahoma	70,917,000
Washington	63,213,000
Ohio	60,993,000
Montana	57,726,000
South Dakota	52,572,000
Indiana	35,896,000
Colorado	34,627,000
United States, total	1,123,143,000

Plains area where hard, red winter wheat is produced, and the northern Great Plains area of the United States and Canada which produces mostly hard, red spring wheat (Fig. 18). Harvesting begins in June in the south and progresses northward until September when it ends in Canada. To the above region we should also add the Pacific Northwest, or more specifically the Columbia Plateau of southeastern Washington and northeastern Oregon (Fig. 18). The climate is relatively mild over those low, rolling hills and the soil is deep. Hard, red spring wheat and hard, red winter wheat make up most of the crop in this latter area, but considerable quantities of the soft wheat varieties, such as white club, are also grown in certain localities.

Canada leads the world in the exportation of wheat. Her huge, impressively mechanized production and small population favor this accomplishment. Her farmers have utilized the resources of their vast acreage in a very effective manner by means of powerful tilling and harvesting machinery. A very large proportion of Canadian wheat and its products as well as that of the United States reaches world trade by way of ports on the Great Lakes. Minneapolis is the continent's greatest interior milling center, in which especially spring wheat is processed.

Considerable soft winter wheat is grown east of the southern portion of the Great Plains wheat farms, even to the Atlantic coast. This eastern area lies, in the main, between the cotton belt and the corn belt and the pasture areas on the north. The wheat grown there reflects the influence of the milder, more humid climate in that it is not quite as good as the hard wheats for bread making, but highly prized for pastries.

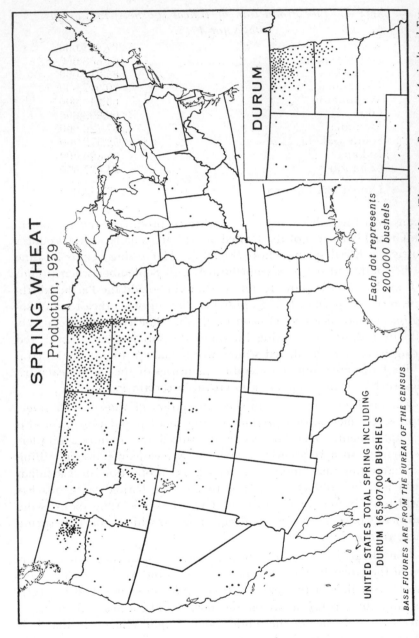

Fig. 19. Location and production of spring wheat in the United States in 1939. (Photo from Bureau of Agricultural Economics, U. S. Department of Agriculture.)

The successful cultivation of wheat within such wide latitudinal and longitudinal limits as indicated in the preceding sections reflects the astounding adaptability of this remarkable crop to climate and soil. The best conditions for wheat production are, however, to be found in the areas of warm summers and subhumid and semiarid climates and in the deep, rich, black and brown soils of continental interiors. These are included mostly within the middle latitude steppes and prairies of the world. These climatic and soil characteristics, it is to be remembered, are also those of the great natural grasslands of the middle latitudes especially in the northern hemisphere. To be sure, wheat is grown in important quantities in the cool, humid climate of northwestern Europe, and it thrives in the cool, dry season of the monsoonal climate of China. It is the coincidence of high temperature and high humidity that is most detrimental to the successful culture of wheat. For this reason, wheat is not grown in abundance in northeastern India, southeastern United States, or in the far northern, subtropical part of Argentina.

The annual precipitation in the great wheat-growing regions of the world is commonly less than thirty inches. Much wheat is produced under a system of dry-land agriculture where the precipitation is as low as 15–10 inches. This system, although uncertain at its best, is made possible in many areas by allowing the fields to rest, that is, to remain free of crop or *fallow* every other year.

Wheat does best when it is grown in a fertile, loamy soil that is well-drained but has a good water-holding capacity. Plenty of phosphorus and nitrogen are required, the first is required for better production of grain, while the latter element improves the quality and increases the protein content of the grain. These values are supplied, it would seem, in almost magic relationships by the Chernozem and Chestnut soils of the primeval grassland areas that have become the great centers of production.

Students of the cereals have recognized for thousands of years the biological kinship of wheat with all the other grasses that are so widely distributed over the earth. Many different varieties of wheat can be traced back to the Grecian botanist Theophrastus, who wrote of their presence in Sicily, Libya, Thrace, Egypt, and Assyria as early as the third century B.C. Two or three centuries later other famous naturalists, such as the Romans Columella, Pliny, and Varro, respected the work of Theophrastus and added to his contributions. These and other men of ancient times distinguished wheats that were bearded and others that were "smooth" or beardless, those that produced red

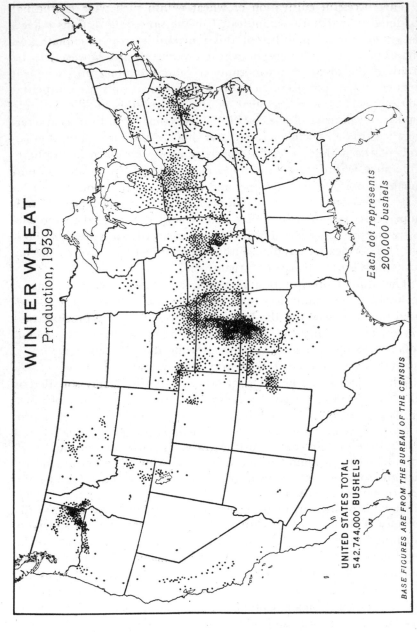

Fig. 20. Location and production of winter wheat in the United States in 1939. (Photo from Bureau of Agricultural Economics, U. S. Department of Agriculture.)

kernels, and others with white grain, those that were early and others late. Summer types and winter types were recognized and some that produced the best grain for food, others that were not as easy to digest. Some of them (*Triticum*) were freed from the chaff in the threshing process; others (*Tar*) retained the chaff after threshing.

Following the important contributions of the ancients to the classification of wheat, the world lapsed into that long period of many centuries, the Dark Ages, when little was done to extend and improve man's knowledge of natural history. Writers who followed the Dark Ages mostly copied and rearranged the work of the ancients without adding much that was new. The great French botanist, Tournefort, commonly regarded as the father of the wheat genus, *Triticum,* was one of the outstanding writers of the early modern period. He published an important book known as *Institutiones Rei Herbariae,* in 1719. He gave a good description of *Triticum* in that book and listed fourteen species of wheat as belonging to this genus.

The work of the Swedish botanist Linnaeus was very important in shaping the general tendencies that have marked the development of the modern classification of plants and animals. Linnaeus published a great book entitled *Species Plantarum* in 1753 in which he attempted to describe the then known plants of the world. He recognized the word *triticum* that Theophrastus had used many centuries earlier, adopted this as the generic name, *Triticum,* for wheat and described seven species under this genus. The seven original Linnaean species of wheat are: *T. aestivum, T. hybernum, T. turgidum, T. polonicum, T. spelta,* and *T. monococcum.* Linnaeus called *T. aestivum* Awned Spring Wheat and *T. hybernum* Smooth Winter Wheat.

Many suggestions were made concerning the classification of wheats by other scientists for a hundred years after Linnaeus, with a tendency as might be expected, to recognize numerous additional species and varieties. Thus Koernicke and Werner, two Germans, in 1885 recognized 150 varieties in eight different groups. Eleven years later Edward Hackel, a noted German agrostologist, grouped the various forms of wheat, *Triticum,* as follows with three species, and their races and sub-races:

> *Triticum sativum*
>   *tenax*
>   *vulgare,* Common Wheat
>   *compactum,* Club Wheat
>   *turgidum,* Poulard Wheat
>   *durum,* Durum Wheat

> *dicoccum,* Emmer
> *spelta,* Spelt
> *Triticum polonicum,* Polish Wheat
> *Triticum monococcum,* Einkorn

Since Hackel's time the classification of the wheats has been largely dominated by agronomists and wheat breeders who have been interested in the effort to classify the species, varieties, and forms that are recognized in cultivation and by genetical studies. A late classification, based on the number of chromosomes, suggests fifteen species. Hundreds of cultivated varieties have been identified; in fact 212 varieties are discussed in one of the late American publications, as being grown somewhere in the United States. While more than two hundred varieties are grown in this country, and some wheat is grown in nearly all of our states, yet the most frequent kinds produced in an important degree are Common Wheat, *T. vulgare,* Club Wheat, *T. compactum,* and Durum Wheat, *T. durum.* Poulard Wheat, Polish Wheat, Emmer, and Spelt are grown sparingly for livestock. Constant breeding tends to develop new varieties that may be better, for various reasons, than any that have been grown. More than fifty improved varieties have been distributed to the farmers in the United States in the last ten years.

The improvement of wheat has been one of the notable and profitable features of crop improvement in general that has characterized agronomic work during the past forty years. It has very recently been reported that Romanian wheat breeders have developed a new variety which produces kernels that are almost three times the weight of ordinary wheat grains! The new form is also said to be highly resistant to fungous diseases. It has been named *Triticum sovieticum,* or Soviet Wheat. Recent reports state that breeders in Russia have produced a perennial variety of wheat, which is of great interest and possible significance.

The combined wheat interests of the United States have developed certain standards by which the varieties of wheat are divided into five commercial groups. These groups of varieties are:

1. HARD RED SPRING WHEAT. These are grown in the northern states and Canada where severe winter weather is dangerous to winter wheat culture (Fig. 21). One of the most notable of these varieties is the world-famous *Marquis.* These are probably the finest of all wheats for bread making.

2. DURUM WHEAT. These are represented by several varieties that are grown also in the northern states especially in the Dakotas, eastern

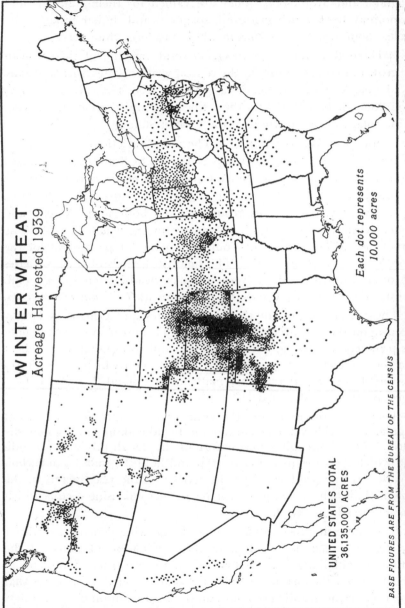

WINTER WHEAT
Acreage Harvested, 1939

Each dot represents
10,000 acres

UNITED STATES TOTAL
36,135,000 ACRES

BASE FIGURES ARE FROM THE BUREAU OF THE CENSUS

Fig. 21. Showing acreage of spring wheat harvested in 1939. *(Photo from Bureau of Agricultural Economics, U. S. Department of Agriculture.)*

Montana and Minnesota. They are valued for their granular flour (semolina) from which macaroni, spaghetti and similar products are made. Some varieties of Durum wheat produce white kernels.

3. HARD RED WINTER WHEAT. Several varieties of these wheats are grown in large quantity in the central western states, such as Texas, Oklahoma, Kansas, and Nebraska (Figs. 20, 22). They also make very good flour for bread. In 1944 these wheats occupied about 47 per cent of the total acreage in wheat in the United States.

4. SOFT RED WINTER WHEAT. The many varieties of these wheats are grown in the eastern states, especially east of Kansas and Nebraska and north of Tennessee and North Carolina. Certain of these varieties are also grown in Oregon, Washington, Idaho, and western Montana.

5. WHITE WHEAT. This group includes both spring wheats and winter wheats. They are grown mostly in the Pacific states. The kernels are white, and so the flour is popular for pastry and for the processing of breakfast foods. The smallish kernels of these varieties are often formed in short, very compact heads, often called "club wheat," though they are technically known as *Triticum compactum.*

The wheat industry of the United States and Canada is largely based upon the hard, red spring wheats. This great industry includes the production, trading, milling, baking, and transportation of wheat and the products of its grain. The variety upon which this industry has largely developed came originally from Poland, by way of Germany, Scotland, and Canada.

The flour produced from the grain of these varieties is the most popular and widely used material for bread-making throughout the world. The elastic, glutenous nature of the dough produces a condition which increases its power to trap and hold the bubbles of carbon dioxide gas that are formed by the activity of the yeast plants in the dough. This behavior largely explains the desired rising quality which characterizes light bread.

It is interesting to recall here how the growing demand for whiter and lighter bread has resulted in the elimination of much of the natural, original, nutritive qualities of the wheat kernel. This demand brought about the abandonment of the old-fashioned buhr stones that were used in the grinding of flour and their substitution by steel rollers in the modern milling industry. The steel roller process made possible the utilization of the hard wheats for flour, whereas the older process was suitable only for the softer varieties.

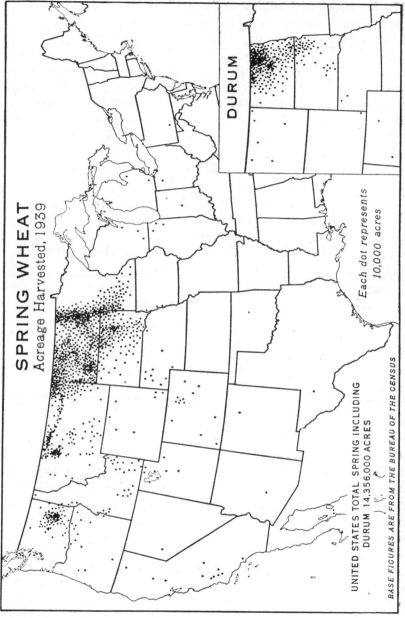

SPRING WHEAT
Acreage Harvested, 1939

DURUM

Each dot represents
10,000 acres

UNITED STATES TOTAL SPRING INCLUDING
DURUM 14,356,000 ACRES

BASE FIGURES ARE FROM THE BUREAU OF THE CENSUS

Fig. 22. Location and acreage of winter wheat harvested in 1939. (*Photo from Bureau of Agricultural Economics, U. S. Department of Agriculture.*)

The improved steel milling or "patent" process of flour manufacture contributed directly to an enormous expanse in the production of the hard wheats and the popularization of light, white bread. The introduction of large-scale commercial baking, and the use of quick-acting yeasts further contributed to the popularity of this important human food. Variations in the methods of milling the flour and preparation of the dough make possible the production of various kinds of bread. A physician by the name of Graham (1794–1851) contended that the most healthful bread was made from the flour resulting from grinding the *entire* kernel of wheat. This flour, composed of all parts of the grain, including the bran and the germ, came to be known as "Graham" flour. We now have "whole wheat" or "entire wheat" bread made from "whole wheat" or "entire wheat" flour. These latter terms are somewhat misleading because a *part* of the *bran* has been removed in the milling process. In making the original Graham flour nothing was removed from the grain, so that this kind of flour was really *the* whole wheat flour.

Standard "patent" flour made by the mills may lack as much as 30 per cent of the original grain and much that is of great nutritional value. This most popular brand of flour has had all of the bran and other portions of the outer tissues and also the embryo or "germ" removed. Certain brands of white flour that are popular for making the lightest breads and cakes may not retain more than 50 per cent of the original entire wheat kernels. The so-called bran flour and germ-of-wheat flour are specially processed in order to retain large proportions of those parts of the grain while the white tissue or flour tissue has been greatly reduced.

The wheat bread made from the stone-ground flour of yesteryears was rather heavy and dark. We have noted that efforts to improve wheat for human food were directed for a long time toward making lighter and whiter bread by eliminating many of those ingredients of the whole wheat kernel which interfered with that desire. Efforts to popularize "whole" wheat bread, bran bread, bran breakfast food and germ-of-wheat bread are familiar to all of us. This movement stresses the contention that the current roller milling processes result in the elimination of many of the natural, rich materials that the wheat kernel originally contains. These food values include such important items as fats, proteins, minerals, and vitamins. It is reasoned that these items—some twenty of them—are needed to make fine, healthy and strong wheat plants. Since they contribute important and necessary values for man too, they ought to be retained. The pure, white, and very light bread that bakeries turn out in enormous quantity to meet the popular demand is, indeed, not nearly as nutritious as the breads that are made from flour containing more nearly all of the material that nature builds into the kernels.

We are hearing much about "enriched bread." This is the latest demonstration of our interest in the composition of wheat flour, and especially directed toward those essentials that we have so long tended to eliminate from most of our white flour and bread. "Enriched" bread is merely bread made from flour from which the above nutritional values have been removed by the original milling processes and *to which,* then, artificially prepared minerals and vitamins have been added. This seems incongruous, does it not? Intelligent people living in a "scientific age" remove so much of the natural nutritive values formed in the grain by the wheat plant, and then attempt to restore artificially the extracted materials to the flour! But it works. Consequently, we may have our white bread, which so many people prefer, after the eliminated natural values have been in part restored with considerable fuss and expense by the development of an entirely new and complicated type of processing. There are still doubts, however, if the highly processed, much advertised, and artificially modified bread is really as good for us as is the nearly naturally complete product.

World-wide shortages of foods, of both vegetable and animal origin, focus attention sharply upon the practices that are involved in the processing of foods. When wheat is scarce nations strive to utilize more of the complete values of the grain by legally requiring the millers to include a larger quantity of the whole grain in the flour. Suggestions are made at such times that meat production be reduced because man receives a much larger return from the foods of the grain if it is used directly for human consumption rather than by feeding it to livestock to produce meat.

CHAPTER 4

Rice

THERE ARE A GREAT MANY REASONS WHY RICE SHOULD BE CITED AS THE most important food-producing organism of all of the world's living things. Certainly, rice might be regarded as the most important plant that man has yet come to know. The word rice is synonymous with agriculture or food in Chinese and other oriental languages. Disliked, detested, and hated by many men of the West, it has for countless centuries been revered and tenderly cultured by the men of the East as their most significant crop. Rice prospers best where the bread grains fail because of too much water and too high temperature. Rice is the only staff of life in large areas of those vast sweating lands of the Old World where people perpetually live close to the marshes and under the constantly enervating influence of tropical humidity and heat. For untold ages, this plant has dominated the philosophy, history, agriculture, economics, and general social life of the Far East.

The earliest cultivation of rice as a tropical and subtropical grass that now yields enormous suplies of nutritious grain for human food, is buried in the uncertain dimness of prehistoric ages. For at least 4,000 years the crop has been grown in China by pitifully primitive methods, and at the same time with very intensive application. Several species of the common genus of Rice, *Oryza,* grow wild in widely separated areas of the tropics of both the Old World and the New World. The modern cultivated varieties of rice probably originated from one of these wild forms that originally grew in China, India, or Africa.

Rice is the one tremendously important and really indispensable food for more than one-half of the world's population. These human beings are largely congregated within the world's major center of rice production and mostly under the influence of the monsoon type of climate in India, China, and the lands to the east and south, including Japan, Korea, the Philippines, Burma, Thailand, Indo-China, British

Malaya, and the Dutch East Indies. The densest populations in the world are found upon the rice lands of the Orient. That vast region produces about 90 per cent of the world's crop of rice. In many portions of those far-flung areas of the "empire of rice" (Fig. 24) this cereal furnishes between 80 to 90 per cent of the food supply of the people. Rice-lands support about one-third of the population of the earth, although only about eight per cent of the land surface of the earth is included in such lands. Small areas of rice culture also occur in the Po Valley of northern Italy, in the Near East, in Africa, and in widely scattered areas of tropical South America. The crop is also seen in the dry, hot lands of Afghanistan and Iran and locally along the central Dnieper in Russia. The Malabar coast of southwest India is an important area of production which is more or less isolated from the great center of rice culture farther to the east. This narrow exposed coastal strip catches the full effect of the torrential rains that fall

FIG. 23. The rice plant, showing portions of the stem, leaves, and the spikelet *(from Hitchcock)*.

there during the wet period of the monsoon in May, June and July.

There is nowhere else on the globe where a single crop is of such immense importance to men as is rice in the Orient. Wheat is of great significance in the newer western world, of course, but wheat is usually only one item in a widely varied diet in the Occident. In the Orient, rice is not only the principal dish of practically every meal for all classes over vast areas, but very often it is the only dish in the monotonous and incomplete dietary. When the rice crop is short, millions starve. Wheat competes with rice only in certain parts of central and north China where the former is grown during the dry period of the monsoonal year. Wheat does not tolerate the high humidity and high temperature of the humid phase of the monsoon type of climate.

The relative importance of rice in the East as compared to the West is reflected in the per capita consumption in different countries. The Siamese and Japanese use from 300 to 400 pounds of rice per capita per year, and the people of the Philippines more than 200 pounds. The use of rice in Java, Thailand, Chosen, and India is slightly less, but in the United States the per capita consumption is only about six pounds per year. The social and economic implications involved in these wide contrasts could be expanded into a major thesis. Let us only state that the "accidents of climate and soil" inherited by the oriental that made him a rice farmer, and those climatic conditions which shaped the destinies of the occidental as he became a grower of wheat, potatoes, barley, corn, swine, cattle, and sheep, are tragically significant in this contrast.

Although rice is still, and probably always will be, the distinctive dish of most of the Orient, we are aware of the fact that nearly everyone eats some rice today, no matter where he may dwell. But, strangely enough, there are places even in China where rice is practically unknown and where wheat, the magic grain of the west, has been introduced with signal success. The culture of rice spread westward and northward from its oriental birthplace at an early date, until it became familiar in India, Babylonia, Egypt, and Europe. Rice was grown in Italy near Pisa as early as 1468 A.D. An experimental planting of rice was made in South Carolina in 1694 from seed said to have originated in Madagascar. From the former area it promptly spread over the subtropical areas of North Carolina, Georgia, Florida, Alabama, and eventually to the black prairie soil of southern Mississippi and Louisiana. Soon after the Civil War the production of rice in Louisiana rapidly increased until that state became the leading producer. Further expansion took the crop to southeastern Texas about 1900, to the river lowlands of eastern Arkansas in 1905, and to the interior valley of California about 1912. Louisiana still leads all of our states in the production of rice. The success of the crop there is indicated by the fact that production in the United States at present exceeds the home demand. Americans should learn to appreciate the value of rice more fully.

The hot, humid tropical and subtropical climates are best suited to the intensive production of rice. High temperature, heavy precipitation, and extensive areas of low, rich, wet soils, or soils that may be flooded, favor the successful cultivation of rice on a large scale. The monsoon type of climate that dominates vast areas of south and south-

east Asia is especially conducive to the noteworthy success of the millions of Oriental rice farmers. Two, or even three, crops of rice are grown in certain especially favored areas in a single year. Large crops are produced in some areas year after year without any special fertilization of the soil, although "night soil" is widely used. In somewhat cooler, less humid areas rice sometimes alternates with wheat during the dry period of the cropping program. High humidity, high temperature, and the very moist soil that are demanded by rice during its growing season are inimical to the culture of wheat.

Fig. 25. Transplanting rice in Japan. (*Photo from Bureau of Plant Industry, Division of Cereal Crops and Diseases, U. S. Department of Agriculture.*)

Rice can be grown most successfully only in soils that will hold water over the surface for considerable periods and which, too, may be quickly and completely drained in order to facilitate the harvesting of the crop. Rich, rather heavy, clay soils or dark, alluvial soils that may be readily puddled or that have impervious subsoils are preferred for rice. A dependable supply of fresh irrigation water is an indispensable requirement for proper rice production in the United States and elsewhere. The fields are flooded soon after seeding and again when the plants are six to ten inches tall. The seedlings are often grown in a nursery as is common in Oriental practice, and from there transplanted by hand directly to the flooded fields (Fig. 25). The fields are then kept flooded with fresh water until the crop is nearly mature, some three to five months later. The fields are drained as the crop heads out and the grain nears maturity so that the soil will dry sufficiently to permit harvesting by hand or by the use of harvesting machinery. Rice is the only major crop that is grown under these conditions. Certain varieties of rice are grown on a small scale in upland soils, like other cereals, but heavy precipitation during the growth of the crop is necessary to make this possible at all.

Power machinery, much like that used on wheat farms, is commonly used in the United States by the growers of rice. Airplanes have been used to sow the grain in California. The Orientals commonly harvest the crop by hand sickle or scythe and thresh the grain by hand with flails or other improvised hand-power machinery.

FIG. 26. Harvesting rice in Japan, hand labor. (*Photo from Bureau of Plant Industry, Division of Cereal Crops and Diseases, U. S. Department of Agriculture.*)

Most of the work of preparing the rice fields in the Orient for sowing, tending, weeding, harvesting, and threshing the crop is done with a vast amount of patient hand labor, much of it by women, by the aid of primitive implements (Figs. 26, 27). These activities are sometimes accompanied by special ceremonies or rituals with a religious trend. Rice culture in the Orient illustrates a type of subsistence agriculture in its most intense degree. Birds destroy much of the grain in many places if vigorous measures are not taken to scare them away.

The low, swampy rice fields in the Orient are often known as *paddies,* in distinction to the far less important and drier *upland rice.* The famous broad river deltas of southeastern Asia present nearly ideal conditions for the growth of paddy rice. In those regions the rice plants are often transplanted from the nursery by hand, by women and men working in the water that covers the fields. In the mountainous areas of Japan, the Philippines, South China, Burma, and Java, the hillsides are often carefully and intricately terrace so that rice may be grown on the flooded terraces more or less as it is grown in the paddies or the flat lands. The terraced fields are flooded by directing the water from the upper levels to those lower down the slopes. Where water is not readily obtained from some natural source above such terraced slopes it must be pumped there, oftentimes by laborious manpower methods.

Fig. 27. Threshing rice in Japan with the use of a cylindrical machine driven by foot-power. *(Photo from Bureau of Plant Industry, Division of Cereal Crops and Diseases, U. S. Department of Agriculture.)*

It is said that the average Chinese peasant family requires about 2,400 pounds of rice per year, and that such yield may be secured from one and one-half acres under the most favorable conditions. The intensive, constant care and the extensive employment of hand labor, usually with primitive tilling, harvesting and threshing implements, that mark the rice culture of the Orient, are truly impressive (Figs. 25, 26, 27). If a proper valuation of the individual human effort could be suggested for the production of rice by these methods we would probably find that it actually costs much more to produce rice than it does to produce wheat in the West with all the modern methods of agriculture and the very effective power machinery that have been developed around the latter commodity under our western conditions.

The total annual world production of rice ranges from 6.0 to 7.5 billion bushels (Table 3). About 90 per cent of the rice crop of the world is grown in the Far East. Agricultural statistics usually credit China with the greatest production of rice among the nations of the world. The figures are uncertain and the estimate is probably low, but China is reported as producing about 3,500,000,000 bushels of rice in one year, or about 38 per cent of the world's yield. India was second in 1945 with 1,900,000,000 bushels and 32 per cent. Next is Japan (plus Chosen) with more than 835,000,000 bushels, and then French Indo-China, 432,215,000; Java with 306,930,000; Burma, 134,-000,000; South America, 160,000,000; Philippine Islands, 75,000,000; Africa, 111,000,000; United States, 75,000,000, of which about one-half is grown in Louisiana; Texas, 18,000,000 in 1945; Italy, 14,950,000, and Egypt, 42, 454,000. Normally Burma, Siam, and French Indo-China supply about 90 per cent of the rice that enters international trade.

TABLE 3.—*The Production of Rice (bushels) in Various Countries and the World, for 1945–46 except where noted otherwise.*

China	2,160,000,000
India	1,900,000,000
Japan and Chosen	432,215,000
French Indo-China (1935–1940)	316,038,000
Java and Madoera (1935–1940)	306,930,000
South America	160,700,000
Burma	134,455,000
Africa	111,000,000
Philippine Islands	75,000,000
United States	70,160,000
Egypt	42,454,000
Madagascar	37,722,000
Italy	14,950,000
World, total, very uncertain	6,278,000,000

The heaviest grower in South America, Brazil, produced 115,113,000 bushels in 1945, which was considerably more than was produced by the United States in the same year. Conditions caused by World War II greatly stimulated the production of rice in the Americas when in 1945 the output was about 50 per cent above the prewar production.

There are thousands of varieties of cultivated rice, including forms of both paddy rice and upland rice. India alone is said to grow 1,100 or more varieties, while China, Japan, the Philippines, the East Indies, and other parts of the world add hundreds of others. Cultivated rice is rather unusual among cultivated plants, however, in that all of the thousands of varieties are regarded as belonging to a few original species, the most important of which is *Oryza sativa*. This is the typical species of the distinctive tribe of grasses known as the *Oryzeae*, or in general, the rice grasses.

The following summary indicates the relationships of some of the more common species and varieties of rice now in cultivation and certain closely related wild species.

> *Oryza sativa,* Cultivated Rice
>   *Utilissima*
>   *Communis,* Large-grain Rice
>   *Minuta,* Small-grain Rice
>   *Glutinosa,* Wild Rice
> *Oryza granulata,* Wild Rice
> *Oryza officinalis,* Wild Rice

The various forms of cultivated rice differ as to being bearded or beardless (smooth), early or late, long-grain or short-grain, glutenous or non-glutenous, and upon many other technical differences. The "wild rice" of the northern United States, *Zizania aquatica*, also belongs to this tribe of grasses, but is an altogether different plant from the species indicated. It is a perennial and is also truly aquatic, being found in the marshlands, especially of Wisconsin and Minnesota.

In the United States rice is threshed by machines which are much like the ordinary threshers used for wheat and oats. The grain as it comes from the thresher is enclosed by the "hull" or "husk" consisting of the closely overlapping, harsh, dry lemma and palea of the original one-flowered spikelet. This *rough rice* is used for seed and is fed to livestock without further processing.

The preparation of rough rice for human food commonly involves several highly specialized methods of treatment in the rice mill or by relatively simple treatment by hand under the most primitive pattern of culture in the Orient. Particles of sand, soil, weed seeds, light grain, and other impurities are first removed by screening or winnowing by hand. The hulls are then broken by hulling stones, and removed by blowers, thus leaving the hulled kernels that are known as cleaned rice or "brown rice." The hulls are often removed in Oriental countries by rubbing the grain in the hands or by gently pounding it with sticks, flailing, or even tramping it with the bare feet.

The hulled grain is then sent through machines (also known as hullers) in which the epidermis of the kernels and parts of the sub-epidermal bran tissue (the *gluten* cells) and the germ are removed. The bran flakes and other fragments of the outer tissues removed by this process are screened out. The grains are given further treatment of this sort in another set of hullers. By this time practically all fragments of the bran and other investing tissues and the germ have been removed, and only the hard, pearly-white starchy tissue is left. The grain is next treated by polishing machines which remove still more of the gluten cells and much starchy tissue and these fragments are discarded by further screening. After this the grains are conveyed to cylinders in which they are steamed and coated with glucose, chalk or talc in order to produce the final product which is again screened, graded, weighed, and bagged. Several commercial grades of rice are distinguished by the presence of whole or unbroken kernels. The best grade is known as "whole rice" or "head rice," and other grades are indicated in which the kernels are marred by variations in the brilliance of polish, color, or size of the kernels.

The highly conditioned rice resulting from the above processing is demanded by Americans and most others. It lacks practically all of the natural nutritive qualities (proteins, fats, minerals, vitamins) which lie in the outer tissues of the kernels that are removed by the processing. As much as 80 per cent of the thiamin, 50 per cent of the riboflavin and 65 per cent of the niacin may be removed by these processes. These values (vitamin B) are to be secured only if we use the *whole grain,* commonly known as *brown rice* that is prepared by hand or as it comes from the initial hullers. This is readily accomplished by the Oriental who hulls the rough rice as he needs it by pounding it in a mortar with a wooden mallet and winnowing it by hand. We Westerners insist that our rice be treated by the further expensive processes, briefly outlined above, that denaturize this valuable food and only transform it into a "more beautiful" product.

The rice may be "enriched" after milling and processing by the addition of some of the vitamins and minerals that were removed by the treatment. As a matter of fact the most nutritious product of our "civilized" processing technique of rice is removed in the coats of the kernels and the germs that come away as bran. The *polish,* or granular material which results from the milling and scouring of the grain is very nutritious and it is sometimes used in gravies, sauces, and puddings, and mixed with meat in sausages. Some of it eventually winds up in the manufacture of soaps and buttons. Thus we see how far modern man goes in his debasement of one of nature's most nutritious foods. He sometimes falls victim to such senseless and expensive ruthlessness, if he persists in using large quantities of the highly processed rice in his daily diet, which can lead to the vitamin-deficiency malady, the dreaded beri beri.

Rice flour and the fragments of the kernels that are produced by the milling processes are used for a wide variety of purposes, such as commercial starch, cosmetics, confections. They turn up in the textile industry, and in the preparation of paste, glue, alcohol, vinegar, and stock foods. The "arrack" of India and the "sake" of Japan are well-known alcoholic beverages made from rice. Rice straw is used for stock food. When the crop is cut by hand, the straw may be kept straight and smooth and it is then widely used in the Orient for the fabrication of mats, screens, hats, coats, sandals, and ropes. The hulls are also useful as packing and insulating material; for mulch, cardboard, fertilizer; and even for fuel. The distinctive and popular *rice paper* of commerce is not made from rice at all but from the pith or pith-like tissue of certain quite different Oriental plants. A more or less similar paper that is now widely used in the United States for cigarettes is made from the fiber of the flax plant.

CHAPTER 5

Indian Corn

A WIDE VARIETY OF THOUGHTS AND EMOTIONS ARE SUGGESTED BY THE simple, very old word, *corn*. There is no more significant organic symbol of American civilization than Indian Corn or Maize. Maize would be a more appropriate and significant element with which to decorate our coins and to use in other typical American symbols than the eagle. Maize has marched with man throughout his conquest and settlement of the western hemisphere and has directly supplied invaluable materials for that accomplishment. It supplies a body-building grain for billions of sleek livestock and gorgeously feathered fowls. It contributes unique food for mankind and supplies countless articles of global barter that now affect scores of millions of men throughout the world. Corn has been a mighty factor in the evolution of economic and industrial strength in America. Indian Corn, in one or more of its manifold relationships, plays a greater part in man's civilization than any other single crop now grown by man (Figs. 28, 29).

The corn plant (Figs. 28, 29) originated in the Americas centuries before the western voyages of Lief Ericson and Christopher Columbus. Modern research tends to indicate that it first appeared in the lowlands of tropical South America at a time long antedating the advance civilization of the Incas. It spread to the farms of the higher, drier Andean climates where it was first cultivated. Then it marched northward to Central America and North America where its high state of culture marked the advanced civilization of the Mayas and the Aztecs. The arts and ceremonies of those ancient peoples were graced by the prominent use of corn, as is evidenced by numerous findings that have rewarded the zeal of archaeological investigators. Corn was grown by the North American Indians on the Rio Grande as early as 700 A.D., and by other tribes of Red Men in New England in the year 1,000. The discovery of America by Europeans was, indeed, a very late "discovery" of *corn*. The plant was unknown in the Old World until it was taken there by the early explorers of the western hemisphere.

Soon after maize was discovered in America it was introduced into Spain, France, and Italy where it rapidly became popular. Later it marched with travelers to Africa, Persia, Turkey, Arabia, India, China, and finally in the sixteenth century to the East Indies, thus completing its march around the world. Portuguese mariners appear to have taken the lead in the wide distribution of the newly-found grain. The

Fig. 28. The corn plant showing stalk, leaves, ears, and tassel *(from Hitchcock.)*

Fig. 29. An ear of corn with husks, silks, and young kernels, two mature kernels from the cob, and portions of the tassel *(from Hitchcock).*

widespread movement of maize into central Europe seems to have been from Turkey by way of the Balkan countries or the Near East. This geographical feature of the story is reflected by the common name "Turkish Wheat" which is widely used for the plant in many parts of the continent.

The first white settlers at Jamestown, Virginia, in 1607 were probably saved from starvation, and the poorly established colony from complete failure and destruction, by a quantity of corn that was brought to those desperate, early colonists on the James by friendly neighboring Indians. Captain John Smith expressed his gratitude for the gifts from the dusky natives when he stated in July 1607 that: "It pleased God to move the Indians to bring us corn ere it was half ripe to refresh us." Those were probably the first roasting ears ever eaten in America by the whites. Governor William Bradford, of Plymouth Colony, wrote of how a group of Pilgrims under the command of Captain Miles Standish were led, in the late fall of 1620, to Indian corn fields, and to some baskets of corn of "diverce collours" that had been cached by the Red Men. The wide significance of these initial contacts of our forebears with the friendly, primitive, native Americans and their energizing native crop can hardly be overestimated.

Corn is the cereal of greatest production in the West, and it is widely grown over the globe. The crop is scattered more widely through the various climatic types than is wheat, its nearest competitor for world trade. Wheat is grown on a larger acreage for the world as a whole, but corn produces the greater yield. The climatic and soils controls, however, tend to limit the maximum output of corn to rather well-defined centers or "belts" that are found on nearly all of the continents (Fig. 30). The outstanding geographic centers and areas of important production of corn are roughly shown on the map (Fig. 30) and summarized in the following synopsis:

    I. NORTH AMERICA
        1. East Central and Middle-Western
            United States
        2. Mexican Plateau
    II. SOUTH AMERICA
        1. The Argentinian Pampa
        2. The Brazilian Highlands
    III. EUROPE
        1. The Danube Basin, plains of Hungary
            and Romania
        2. The Valley of the Po
        3. Dnieper plains of southwestern Russia
    IV. ASIA
        1. Northern India
        2. China and Manchukuo
        3. French Indo-China
        4. The Java Area
    V. AFRICA
        1. Egypt, valley of the Nile
        2. The Union of South Africa

The United States is the principal center of corn culture and the leading producer of corn of the entire world (Table 5). The magnitude of the nation's corn crop and the meaning of this leadership by our homeland are indicated by the fact that the total yield of corn for the world is now somewhat more than five billion bushels (in 1946–47 the yield was 5,410,000,000 bu.) and that 70 per cent or more of this vast tonnage is grown right here at home. The yield in the United States in 1944 was about 3.2 billion bushels on 97.0 million acres, and in 1945 it was but slightly less on a total area of 91.2 million acres. Corn is, indeed, the *great* American crop!

The main area of corn production in the United States radiates from an irregular, rambling zone that spreads across certain north central and middle-western states that is often spoken of as the "Corn Belt." Roughly, the corn belt (Fig. 31) includes northern Kansas,

TABLE 4.—*The Production of Corn (bushels) in Various States for 1945.*

Iowa	579,442,000
Illinois	407,295,000
Nebraska	329,855,000
Minnesota	253,399,000
Indiana	176,244,000
Missouri	162,554,000
Ohio	142,956,000
South Dakota	140,292,000
Wisconsin	116,536,000
Kansas	114,793,000
United States, total	3,203,310,000

southern and eastern Nebraska, southeastern South Dakota, southwestern Minnesota, Iowa, northern Missouri, the northern half of Illinois, central Indiana, and the western half of Ohio. This area lies between the "Cotton Belt" on the south and the northern "Pasture and Dairy Belt." More than 100 million acres are included in this great land of corn.

Although the acreage of corn is heavily concentrated within the corn belt, it must be understood that corn is also a very important crop in the immediately surrounding territory and in other localities. It is grown to some extent in every state of the Union. In fact the crop is of considerable local importance at least throughout that whole vast territory that marches from the Atlantic Coast of the United States westward to the eastern border of the Great Plains. And, of course, it must not be understood that the corn belt is of significance only

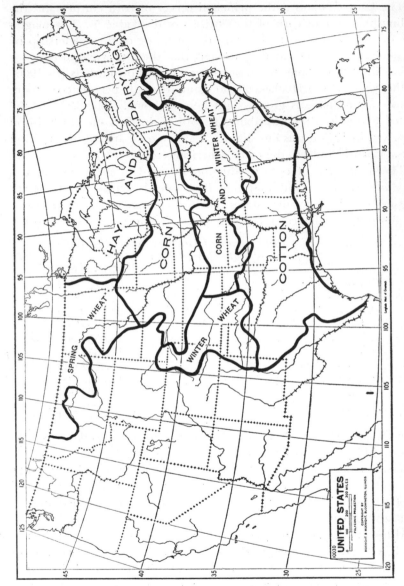

Fig. 31. Location of the corn belt of the United States in its relation to the other great agricultural regions of eastern United States.

because of that one crop, since the same area is probably the most highly developed and diversified *mixed farming* section of the world. Corn is grown to a much more limited extent in all the other states of the Union. Iowa, Illinois, and Nebraska are the leading states in acreage and production of corn, those three states producing 1,316,-592,000 bushels in 1945 (Table 4). The most highly refined and progressive methods of culture and improvement, including the introduction and wide use of hybrid seed, now characterize the management of this important crop in the United States.

Corn is also grown on the high central plateau of northern Mexico. The methods used there are still rather primitive, the fields are small, and the yields are very low. The acreage devoted to corn in Mexico is about 8 million and the annual production about 75 million bushels. Notwithstanding these unfavorable aspects, the crop is of great value there because it is practically all used locally as human food. Corn culture and the utilization of corn products in modern Mexico still reflect practices that date back to prehistoric times in that region.

TABLE 5.—*The Production of Corn (bushels) in Various Countries and the World, for 1945 except as otherwise noted.*

United States	3,018,410,000
China (1935–1939)	272,513,000
Brazil	220,000,000
Romania (1935–1939)	211,890,000
Russia (1930–1934)	153,482,000
Argentina	140,701,000
Yugoslavia	136,000,000
India	98,000,000
Manchuria (1935–1939)	86,586,000
Hungary	80,286,000
Java and Madoera (1935–1939)	79,976,000
Mexico	75,000,000
Union of South Africa	66,964,000
Egypt	66,946,000
Italy	59,052,000
World, total	5,200,000,000

The production of corn in South America is tremendously interesting and significant in many ways. Argentina is the greatest producer there, and the varieties grown are mostly of the flint corn type. That country ranks next to the United States in total yields of corn, annually (1945) growing about 140 million bushels on 11 million

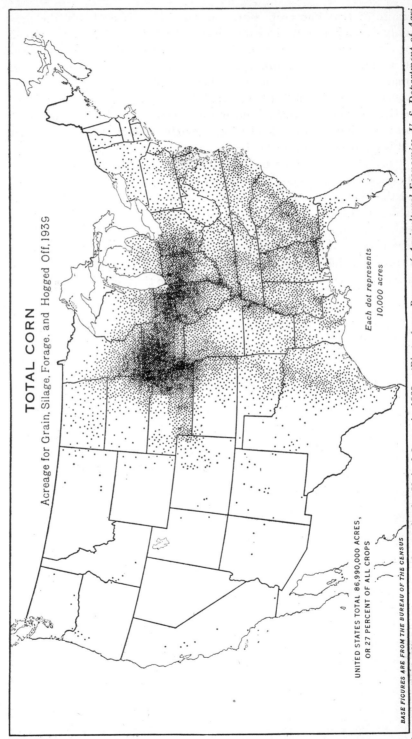

TOTAL CORN

Acreage for Grain, Silage, Forage, and Hogged Off, 1939

Each dot represents
10,000 acres

UNITED STATES TOTAL 86,990,000 ACRES,
OR 27 PERCENT OF ALL CROPS

BASE FIGURES ARE FROM THE BUREAU OF THE CENSUS

Fig. 32. The location and acreage of corn in the United States in 1939. (*Photo from Bureau of Agricultural Economics, U. S. Department of Agriculture.*)

acres, which is about the corn acreage for the state of Iowa. The acreage and yield are very low as compared with the figures for the United States, and yet Argentina is the world's greatest exporter of corn. The Argentinians export about 80 per cent of the corn that they grow, the most of it going to the countries of western Europe. The bulk of this export trade in corn may be as much as forty times the tonnage of corn exported by the United States. In fact, we *import* about as much corn annually as the Argentine uses at home. The reason for Argentina's place as the chief exporter of corn among the nations is due to a combination of conditions. The population is relatively low and the Argentinian livestock men do not feed a great deal of corn, in spite of the fact that an abundance of corn is at hand and is cheap. Yet *grass* is cheaper. With corn cribs bursting the farmers still feel that grass is to be preferred for feeding, so that much livestock is marketed directly from the ranges and pastures. The Argentinians have already embarked upon a program for the increase and improvement of their beef cattle industry, and if this is more or less paralleled by an expansion and improvement of swine, we will probably witness a decrease in their corn export figures in future years. Larger acreages for corn could probably be found if there was a greater demand for the feed for livestock.

The important corn-growing area, the "Corn Belt" of Argentina lies in the north central portion of the vast grain-growing domain of the pampa. This includes especially the northern part of the province of Buenos Aires, Entre Rios, Corrientes, southern Santa Fe, and southeastern Cordoba. This area is about 140 miles long and mostly east of the great wheat crescent of Argentina. Expansion of this corn belt to the north and west is doubtful because of the increasing aridity, but much more corn could probably be grown northeastward and eastward in the more humid Argentinian Mesopotamia, that is, between the Paraguay and Uruguay rivers. Southward the climate becomes too cold for corn.

Conditions that favor corn growing on a large scale in the important area of the pampa of Argentina are the rich, deep, well-drained soils, favorable and seasonable rainfall, and good temperature relations, as well as closeness to market. This area is relatively close to the sea, as compared with the North American corn belt. This is an important factor that contributes to the export trade of Argentina. Much of the rest of Argentina is too dry, or too cold, or too hot for corn, but it is grown to some degree in nearly all parts of the country

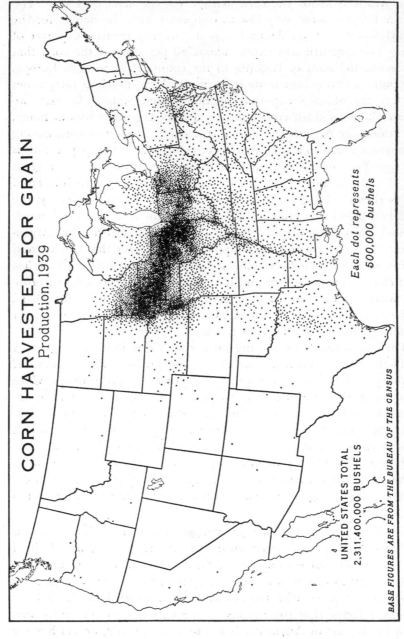

CORN HARVESTED FOR GRAIN
Production, 1939

Each dot represents
500,000 bushels

UNITED STATES TOTAL
2,311,400,000 BUSHELS

BASE FIGURES ARE FROM THE BUREAU OF THE CENSUS

FIG. 33. Location and amount of corn harvested for grain in 1939. (Photo from Bureau of Agricultural Economics, U. S. Department of Agriculture.)

except in Patagonia. Extensive holdings of corn lands under single ownership characterize the corn belt of the pampa. Such corn *estancias* are sometimes as large as 35,000 acres and are farmed by as many as one hundred eighty tenant farmers. The autumn corn picking season in Argentina is in March, April, and May.

Interest in corn culture in Brazil, the largest of the South American states, seems to be increasing in the southeastern part of the country. Brazil's acreage of corn, largely grown in the highlands of the southeast, is about 10 million acres. The three principal corn-growing states are Minas Geraes, Sao Paulo, and Rio Grande du Sol. The cornfields of Brazil are small, widely scattered and, in general, poorly managed, but the country produces about 215 million bushels of the grain annually. Practically all of this is used as human food and for swine. Tropical and subtropical climates and soils, topographic unevenness, and poor farm management combine to make the Brazilian corn crop important only from the standpoint of subsistence agriculture. Under such conditions corn does become an important item in the maintenance of a rather large proportion of the population but on a low standard of living.

The states of the Danube Basin have long been known as producers of staple farm surpluses (Table 5). The region is favored by rainfall and temperature conditions that are similar to those of the North American corn belt, and stands out as one of the most important corn-growing areas of the Old World. Romania, Yugoslavia, Hungary, and Bulgaria together grow corn on about 25 million acres with a yield of around 425 million bushels. Those countries have always used a large proportion of their corn for human food. Corn culture in those areas is now expanding in response to increased attention being given to swine breeding. That region really is *the* corn belt of Europe. The acreage devoted to corn is also on the increase in Germany.

Much of the corn produced in the Po Basin of Italy is grown under irrigation. The yields are rather high under such conditions, sometimes even exceeding the American average. Considerable corn is also grown in Italy on land that is too rough for irrigation, especially southward from the Po. The total acreage is about 3.5 million, and the annual production has been as high as 110 million bushels, 59 million in 1945.

While natural conditions favor limited corn culture in the Dnieper plains of southwestern Russia, the yields there are likely to suffer because of a widespread deficiency of precipitation during the growing season. The acreage of corn in Russia is about 7 million and the production is around 153 million bushels, the average 1930 to 1934.

Corn is widely grown as a local subsistence crop in Asia, but it is definitely much more restricted as an important commercial crop. The irrigated, semiarid areas of the Punjab in northwestern India and the alluvial, well-drained soils of the humid Ganges valley are the principal corn-growing centers of India. Although it is a staple human food in India, corn is grown on only about 7 million acres and the yield was about 98 million bushels in 1945. The yield is very low, amounting to less than 2 per cent of the world's total, but it is of great importance especially to the hill peoples of northern India.

China ranks as a major corn-producing nation. The rather uncertain statistics indicate that eastern and northern China produces about 242 to 272 million bushels on approximately 11 million acres. Corn and soybeans—often planted with corn—are of great importance in China, especially beyond the great rice-producing areas of the warm, humid south and southeast. The less favorable natural conditions in arid Manchukuo reduce corn production to about one-fifth that of China proper, but nevertheless, it is of importance there as a subsistence food crop.

Corn is of considerable importance also in French Indo-China where it is largely grown for human food. A five-year average was 21,000,000 bushels on 1,000,000 acres. That country is even an exporter of corn to a small degree, shipping out about 18.5 million bushels in 1936.

The growing of corn in the East Indies is centered in Java and on the small island of Madoera lying near the north coast of Java. It is an important food for the teeming population of that tropical area, where about 79 million bushels are grown on 5 million acres. Here we have a situation in which corn from the West and rice from the East are in direct competition for the favor of mankind. East and West really do meet at various points on the highways of grassland agriculture and commerce.

As far as Africa is concerned, we find that corn culture has invaded the valley of the Nile and also certain provinces in the southeastern part of the great continent below the equator. Egypt, the Land of the Pharaohs, became a corn-producing area long after the fabled times of those early rulers. Corn is grown on about 2 million irrigated acres in the lower valley of the Nile. The total production there is about 67 million bushels, which is a rather good yield per acre. Corn is usually planted in Egypt in July and picked in late fall.

Corn is grown in several portions of the Union of South Africa but most of it is produced in the rather dry, warm inland plateau region of the provinces, mostly north of Basutoland. The rich corn lands of the Transvaal lie mostly above 2,000 feet in elevation. Considerable corn is also grown in the warm, more humid coastal climate of Natal to the east. The Union of South Africa produces about 67 million bushels of corn on approximately 6 million acres, and this is of major importance for home consumption by the native population. Conditions of world trade would seem to favor an increase in corn production in that region, in spite of the fact that natural conditions for expansion of the crop there are not of the most favorable. The possibilities of hybrid corn should be of great interest to that portion of the world.

The adaptability of corn to a wide variation of climatic types and soils is one of the truly amazing features of this master cereal. Certain varieties of high cereal value in form of grain may be grown where rainfall is 10 inches or less, and where the days are extremely hot, as on the steppes of Russia and in southwestern United States and Mexico. Other varieties are valued in areas where rainfall is heavy and where lower temperatures prevail. In one type or another corn has also become adapted to a wide range of altitude and topography. It is found on low coastal plains, and even in areas below sea level, as well as on the north Caspian plains, and it also thrives at altitudes above 8,000 feet in the rough mountains of Peru and Ecuador. By intensive breeding, varieties and types of corn have been developed that do well under an amazing range of temperature, atmospheric humidity and soil moisture, length of growing season, length of day, and even wind relationships.

In spite of its wide climatic and soils tolerance, corn is a plant that requires relatively high temperature both night and day during the growing season. Where the nights are often too hot for comfortable sleep the corn crop is making its best growth. There must be an abundance of moisture in the soil at the same time, and the humidity must also be relatively high. Even a few days of excessively high temperature, coupled with low humidity and considerable wind may be very destructive during the critical period. Corn is not a good crop for cool climates. Where the growing season is short and cool, wheat, barley, or other kinds of small grains or pasture grasses do better than corn, but even under these conditions as in the northern United States, corn may be grown for silage and fodder.

The characteristic varieties of corn that have been produced reflect the widely divergent nature of the climates concerned. Thus certain types are very short, say two feet, and have few leaves, seven to nine, and require a short season, that is, 60 to 70 days to mature. Other types are tall, say 15 to 20 feet, with 35 to 45 leaves, and require 10 or 11 months to mature. Between such varietal extremes many other varieties reflect relationships to other types of climate and soil. These adaptations are all strongly indicative of the extensive work that corn breeders have done since improvement was begun by the early corn growers of America.

Most of the corn of the globe is grown in the intermediate climates. The crop is most at home in the borderland belts between the typical broadleaf, deciduous woodland climate and the tall-grass prairie type, with a decided preference for the sunnier and less humid features of the latter. But, of course, successful corn culture ranges far beyond this rather narrowly circumscribed belt and into many very different types of climate. The real corn belt of the United States is essentially coextensive with the western half of the area of short-cold-winter, long-hot-summer type of intermediate climates as distinguished by the climatologists Koeppen and Geiger. We find, too, that important corn-growing areas stretch southward into the humid-subtropical, and northeastward into the modified-humid-continental type of New England where corn is an important crop for silage and stover. Our discussion has indicated also that certain varieties of hardy corn are grown westward well within the arid middle-latitude steppe. Corn is grown under the above or in closely related types of climate in most of the other great centers. It is worth mentioning that much of the corn crop of Brazil, India, French Indo-China, and the East Indies grows in the tropical-savanna type of climate. To all these we must add a few additional climatic types, such as tropical-highland and tropical-steppe, to give a more nearly complete summary of the extensive climatic background into which the production of this cosmopolitan master cereal has been carried during the past 450 years.

Corn also adjusts itself to a wide variety of materials and conditions resident in the soil. Soil relationships that are most likely to be critical include an abundance of moisture, good drainage and air supply, fair warmth, and high fertility. Nitrogen and phosphorus are the especially important nutrients supplied the crop by the soil, but corn is also sensitive to a deficiency of magnesium and potash. Soil technologists have distinguished several major types and many varieties of soils that are found here and there in the great corn-growing regions of the globe. The deep, warm, moist, dark and fertile soils of the tall-grass prairie areas of the world are those that supply the best natural conditions for the continued production of the finest crops of corn. These contributions of the soil to the corn crop are furnished in the most nearly ideal degree by the corn belt of the United States. Similar and significant correlations between climatic types, soils, native vegetation, and corn production are notable features of the other great corn-growing areas of the world, as in the Corn Belt of Argentina and the Danube Basin.

In the United States we use the word *corn* exclusively for the common tall, coarse, annual grass that produces its grain in dense, husk-covered *ears* at the axils of one or more of the intermediate leaves, and its pollen in a branching *tassel* or *tossel* at the top of the *stalk*. Less commonly we use the word Indian corn or maize for the plant. In other countries where English is spoken, the word corn generally refers to wheat, and corn in the American sense is regularly called maize. The word *maize* is one of several more or less similar words that have been applied to the plant in the Caribbean region for centuries. The plant was introduced into Europe and other parts of the world with a similar word with a wide variation in spelling such as *mays, mahiz, mais, maiz*. We Americans could easily contribute to desirable standardization, and thereby aid in the elimination of much international confusion by insisting upon the use of the distinctly American word *maize* for this distinctly American plant. It would seem odd and perhaps foolish at first to say "pop maize" and "sweet maize" but surely we could soon get accustomed to this usage.

Soon after the plant appeared in Europe in the sixteenth century it came to be described as "mays" or "maize" by the leading biologists of the time. The searching studies of the great Swedish botanist, Linnaeus, included references to this plant in his publications and he wrote its technical description under the name, *Zea mays* L. The Linnaean designation, which was applied in 1753, is still regarded throughout the world of science as an acceptable technical name for this great American contribution to the list of the most important economic plants of the globe.

The numerous important types, forms, races, or groups of varieties

of maize that are known or grown today are mostly included in six
quite distinctive varieties. These are:

Zea mays tunicata, Pod Corn
Zea mays everta, Pop Corn
Zea mays indenta, Dent Corn
Zea mays indurata, Flint Corn
Zea mays saccharata, Sweet Corn
Zea mays amylacea, Flour Corn

The characteristics and qualities of these (except the first) are
familiar to most people since they are seen in a multitude of forms in
various parts of the world. Pod corn is especially unique because of
the fact that each grain is completely enclosed, even at maturity, by the
greatly enlarged scales of the female spikelet which appear like a
separate set of husks for each individual kernel on the cob. Pod corn
is commonly regarded as a primitive variety. In all of the other
varieties the corresponding scales persist merely as tiny, dry, white or
reddish membranous flakes, about the *basal point* of the kernels.
These dry remnants are usually numerous and prominent on the cob
after the kernels have been shelled off.

Hundreds of forms or types of cultivated corn have been produced
by breeders working with many of the above varieties. By such technical methods and by improvements in field management this great
crop has been fitted into the complicated pattern of the world's climates and soils as has already been noted. One of the most significant
of the recent accomplishments of the breeders of corn has been the
production of hybrid seed corn for practical use on the farm. These
advances are rapidly contributing to the wide adoption of hybrid seed
by our farmers and to the consequent improvement in the crop and
the increase of yields in many parts of the world. The possibilities
for future advances in this line of agricultural science that seem to be
within the early grasp of geneticists and farmers is a subject that we
contemplate with thrilling anticipation. Here is one of the most
valuable contributions of biology to agriculture in the last half century. We see a particulary significant value in this work in these late
years as the world comes to face the fact of shortages of food on a
global magnitude.

Maize is the greatest American contribution to the world's food
supply for man and beast. Early Europeans who came to our shores
and who left records of their observations were impressed by the
unique and numerous values of this great natural product of the Occi-

dent. They were also greatly interested in the methods of production and in the preparation of corn for food as they observed the common practices of the American Indians and the early white settlers.

The Swedish botanist, Pehr Kalm, with the financial and professional assistance of the great master Linnaeus, visited in eastern America from 1748 to 1751. Kalm spent much time around Philadelphia and in New Jersey, and traveled to western Pennsylvania and New York where he studied the cultivation and uses of corn by the Iroquois. Benjamin Franklin aided him in his travels. He also visited Canada for a time as a guest of the French government. Kalm published a very interesting account of his travels and observations on the soil and climatic relationships and uses of maize in America in one of the Swedish governmental publications in 1751 and 1752. He counted the kernels on the ears and familiarized himself with different methods of shelling and preparing the grain in both the green and ripe state for man and beast. Raw, fresh ears, roasting ears, parched corn, corn meal, mush and bread, grits, and the various ways of preparing these foods greatly impressed him, as did the large amount of corn that was grown and used as human food. The mixtures and recipes that Kalm recorded include various types of corn bread and biscuits. They were often made with fresh or dried wild grapes, blueberries, or strawberries truly western delicacies which, in Kalm's description make our mouth's water even now.

The cosmopolitan values of corn have been continually increased and expanded since its discovery by Europeans and its hearty adoption by the American colonists. Amazing new discoveries by the breeders and the fertile imagination and ingenuity of farmers and processers still continue to increase the long list of extremely valuable products of this noteworthy grass. Hundreds of millions of people scattered throughout the world are somehow or other indebted to maize because of the varied and useful products that it contributes to their welfare, though they may be far removed from the farms where the crop is grown.

The United States produces about seventy per cent of the total corn crop of the globe, or about 3 billion bushels. About one-half of this is fed to swine, mostly within the corn belt, but also in large quantities to the pigs of the cotton belt and the areas in which winter wheat and dairy products are the major crops. It is said that about 25 per cent of the beef cattle of our country are also grown in the corn belt. Besides these there are great, colorful herds of dairy cattle and bands of sheep, as well as flocks of poultry without end, all of which consume enormous quantities of corn foods of various kinds. Large quantities of green corn are also cut for silage especially in the northern states. Fodder and stover supply other important items to the types of feed that the farmers of the world secure from this crop. Numerous by-products of the corn milling industry, such as corn-germ meal, corn-oil meal, corn-gluten meal, are valuable feed for livestock.

Although corn is grown as a principal livestock food in most countries, large quantities of the grain are also widely used for human beings. The warm countries such as Mexico, India, and southern China, Brazil and the Balkans, utilize a large proportion of their corn for human consumption. Green corn as roasting ears and for canning purposes, and dried corn in various forms and from numerous varieties are very popular throughout the world. Many varieties of sweet corn and pop corn yield large quantities of delightful foods that are used for human beings exclusively. The annual pack of sweet corn (Fig. 34) in the United States amounts to several hundred million cans. The pop corn crop of 1944 was more than 202 million bushels on 154,000 acres. The popularity and production of these crops are steadily increasing.

Corn meal or flour can scarcely compete with wheat flour for bread making, because it does not make nice light loaves and the bread tends to crumble readily after baking. The reason for this is the lack of gluten in the dough made from corn meal. Nevertheless, the nutritious foods in the form of corn bread, johnny cake, hoe cakes, corn pone, tortillas, mush, hominy, grits, and various breakfast foods are justly popular supplements to the regular diet of breads and pastries made from wheat flour. The crisp, hot tortillas as they are made in Mexico or Texas rank with the finest of the world's unique foods.

The numerous industrial uses of corn and corn products are indeed astonishing. Probably about 100 million bushels of corn are now being used annually in the United States for these purposes. The preparation of corn starch for the laundry and table, corn syrup, corn sugar, corn gluten, and dextrin in increasing quantities illustrates the values in that direction. Dextrin from corn is used in enormous quantities in the preparation of a wide variety of adhesives. Corn starch is the basic fundamental for a long series of edible and industrial preparations. Corn oil is secured from the embryo (germ) of the kernel and has become a very important commodity in the preparation of foods, soaps, plastics, and explosives in recent years. The rich

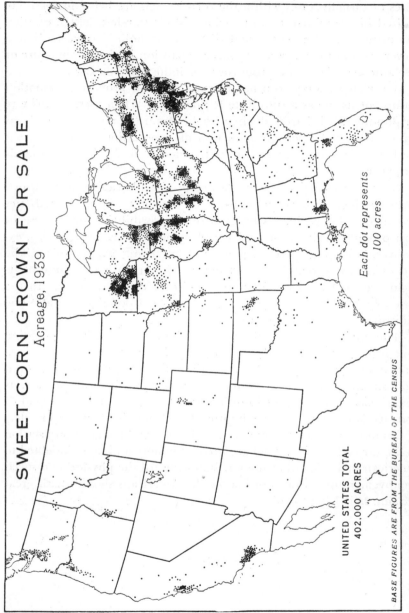

SWEET CORN GROWN FOR SALE
Acreage, 1939

UNITED STATES TOTAL
402,000 ACRES

Each dot represents
100 acres

BASE FIGURES ARE FROM THE BUREAU OF THE CENSUS

Fig. 34. Location and acreages of sweet corn grown for sale in 1939. *(Photo from Bureau of Agricultural Economics, U. S. Department of Agriculture.)*

stores of carbohydrates within the corn kernels are being increasingly utilized in the preparation of various édible starches, jellies, candies, soft drinks, and fermented and distilled alcoholic products. There is every reason to expect a very large expansion in the manufacture of alcoholic materials made from corn for industrial purposes.

A variety of waxy corn has recently received prominent attention because of its use as a substitute for tapioca. When used in this way for puddings, it is hardly distinguishable from the real tapioca. This may in time make possible reduction of importation of tapioca from the Dutch East Indies, which usually amounts to 300 million pounds each year.

Corn is also a prominent feature of the plastics industry which seems destined to develop into one of the most important activities that utilize this grain. Numerous other possibilities for the use of corn products such as for wall board, paper, cordage, upholstery, explosives, adhesives, solvents, and gases are being investigated. The ears of corn are sometimes used for fuel in Argentina, because of its slight use for livestock and the low price of the heavy crop. In the form of moulded briquets, corn is said to be a popular fuel and one with high energy-yielding value.

The numerous and valuable contributions of this outstanding American grass to the welfare of mankind serve to stimulate and intensify further research in the hope that additional, and perhaps even more startling, values may be found among the still uncovered secrets of *Zea mays*. Our insight into the great biological and social field of heredity is constantly being improved and enriched by the breeders of this most important crop plant. Scientists and men of every station in life throughout the world are becoming more and more indebted to American maize for what it contributes toward the physical and social improvement of all races of mankind. Americans should, with great acclaim, hail King Corn!

CHAPTER 6

Barley

BARLEY, OATS, AND RYE ARE SOMETIMES CONSIDERED SECONDARY CE-
reals. This is true only in certain special senses. Oats and barley are
largely grown for foods for livestock, and as such oats is secondary only
to corn in yield, with barley third in that group. Barley, especially
the varieties with soft starchy grain, is a major cereal as a source of
malt in the preparation of beer and similar fermented beverages, and
for malt extract. Oats commonly ranks second only to wheat in yield
in bushels for the world. Rye is of importance as the world's second
most important crop that is used for bread, outranked, as it is, by
wheat both as to preference and production. Wheat leads the list of
cereals in world acreage and is commonly followed by corn, rice, oats,
rye, and barley.

Barley, like wheat, is one of the oldest of cultivated plants. Scholars
tend to agree that this cereal is probably the very oldest of all cultivated plants. Barley flour, ground by stones, was used for bread probably before wheat was used for that purpose. Loaves of bread found
in the ruins of ancient Egypt were composed at least in part of barley.
The origin of malting and the brewing of beer can also be traced back
to the earliest uses of the cereals. Pliny, the ancient Roman scientist
who lost his life in the famous eruption of Vesuvius in 79 A.D., regarded barley as the most ancient of man's foodstuffs.

This important grass (Fig. 35) probably originated in the arid lands
of northern Africa and southwestern Asia. It was widely grown in
ancient times as a bread-stuff and for livestock food. In early times its
culture marched with man to southern, central, and western Europe
where it was the leading grain used for bread until rye and wheat became more popular during the sixteenth century. Barley was brought
to the western world by the early explorers and by the colonists in the
sixteenth and seventeenth centuries. Its noteworthy hardiness con-

tributed to the important early success of the crop in the New World and under the new and untried conditions of those critical years of American history.

The world distribution of barley closely follows that of wheat.

The hardiness of barley adapts it to even a wider range of climatic and soil conditions than wheat, even into high latitudes and high altitudes. But the major centers of production are about the same as those of wheat. It is more dependable in the higher latitudes than wheat, as shown by its growth in northern Scandinavia and toward the Arctic Ocean in Russia. The most striking contrast in the distribution of barley and wheat culture for the world as a whole is reflected by the fact that there is comparatively little barley grown in the southern hemisphere. Some barley of distinctly local importance only is grown in Chile, Afghanistan, Iran, Argentina, and Australia.

FIG. 35. The barley plant showing portions of stems, leaves, heads of smooth and bearded varieties, a group of three spikelets, and a single floret *(from Hitchcock).*

The principal barley centers of the world may be identified by the following list:

    I. THE CHINA AND JAPAN REGION
   II. THE RUSSIA, TURKEY, AND ROMANIA REGION
  III. THE WEST EUROPEAN REGION
        1. The Central and Northern European Area
        2. The Mediterranean Area
  IV. THE NORTHERN INDIA REGION
   V. THE NORTH AMERICAN REGION
        1. The Northern Prairie Area
        2. The California Area

The annual barley crop of the world as a whole now amounts to about 2,100,000,000 bushels (Table 6). Barley is very widely grown over the northern hemisphere, especially across Europe and Asia. China commonly leads all of the areas in barley production, with as much as 43 million bushels, for a recent five-year average. The competition between barley and rice in China is about the same as for wheat and rice. The barley crop grows rapidly and matures in the cool, dry weather of late winter and early spring. In that way it is ready for harvest before the onset of the hot, humid weather of the summer phase of the monsoon that favors the rice crop in those portions of China where both crops are grown. Barley is an important crop in Japan, including Chosen, where it is likewise grown in the cooler, drier part of the year and may thus alternate with rice. It is often grown on slopes too steep for rice. The annual yield of barley in Japan has been as high as 119,000,000 bushels, or about one-third that of China, but is much lower at present. The grain is commonly used in both these countries for human food. The yields of barley per acre in these two countries is only fair, that is, from 22 to 27 bushels per acre.

TABLE 6.—*The Production of Barley (bushels) in Various Countries and the World, for 1945 except as otherwise noted.*

China (1935–1939)	343,158,000
Russia (1930–1934)	270,694,000
United States	263,961,000
Canada	157,757,000
India	107,893,000
Germany (1944)	104,259,000
United Kingdom	98,373,000
Romania (1930–1934)	73,564,000
Japan (1935–1939)	73,149,000
Poland (1935–1939)	65,077,000
Turkey	64,441,000
Denmark	57,411,000
Iran	57,411,000
Morocco (1943)	45,869,000
Argentina	38,581,000
France	34,500,000
Algeria (1943)	34,447,000
Spain	33,300,000
Hungary (1935–1939)	30,178,000
Iraq	29,854,000
World, total	2,100,000,000

Russia commonly ranks second in barley production with about 270 million bushels over a less recent five-year average, but with a yield of only sixteen bushels per acre. Romania produces about 74 million bushels per year at the same yield per acre. The rich Chernozem soils of those countries that are so important for their vast wheat crops also favor barley production. The tendency to aridity sometimes reduces the yield of barley there, but the crop is often mature before great damage has been done by the severe weather. Barley is widely grown in Turkey also, where it does fairly well in the arid climate. Turkey produces about 64 million bushels per year.

The cool climate and good soils of central and northern Europe favor the production of high yields of barley. It is used there both for malting purposes and very importantly as feed for livestock. Germany commonly ranks third among the nations of the world in the production of barley, with about 214 million bushels per year, which is slightly higher than the production in the United States for the same five-year period. Poland, Hungary, France, Great Britain and Denmark also produce considerable barley. It is very important for livestock in those countries, especially in Denmark.

The dry, semitropical climate of southern Spain and northern Africa, as far east as Tripolitania, is conducive to barley production. Winter barley, grown during the humid season of the year and harvested at the beginning of the dry period, is a very important crop for livestock in those areas. The ability of the barley to grow rapidly during cool weather greatly favors the crop for just such lands. Spain normally produces about 110 million bushels, but is down at the present time, Algeria about 35 million, and French Morocco 50 million bushels per year.

The barley crop of the central Ganges region of India is also grown during the less humid, cooler season. The grain is used in large quantities as food for human beings as well as for livestock. India produces, on the whole, about 110,000,000 bushels. Not much barley is grown in the drier, wheat-producing areas southward in the Deccan peninsula portion of India. The crop is grown to a limited extent on the high, arid, and bleak plateaus of Tibet, north of the Himalayas, and it reaches high up on the slopes of those mountains. It is also found on the hot plains of Hindustan.

The United States commonly ranks third or fourth in barley production, with 214 million to 325 million bushels on 13–16 million acres annually. Canada's barley crop ranges upward from 75 million to about 160 million bushels annually. The crop is grown here largely for feed for livestock, along with corn and oats. There are two main centers or belts of barley culture in North America (Fig. 36).

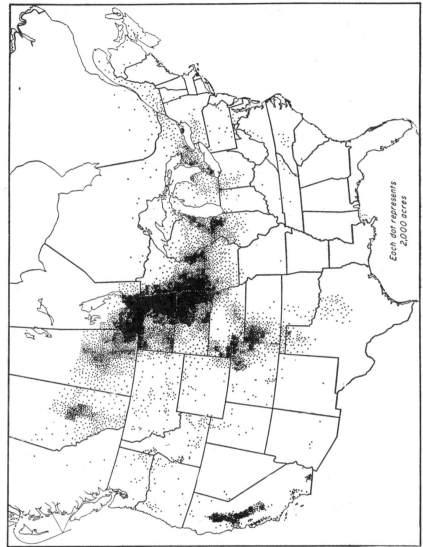

Fig. 36. Location and acreages of barley in the United States and Canada in 1929 and 1930 respectively. (*Photo from Bureau of Plant Industry, Division of Cereal Crops and Diseases, U. S. Department of Agriculture.*)

Each dot represents 2,000 acres

The more important of these is in the northern portion of the prairies, especially western Minnesota, and southern Manitoba, eastern North Dakota, South Dakota, northeastern Nebraska, and northern Iowa. Much barley is also grown eastward from this area through Wisconsin and into Illinois and Michigan. Another important area lies in the rather dry plains of southwestern Nebraska, northwestern Kansas and northeastern Colorado. Spring barley is often grown in the latter area if the wheat crop fails from drought, winterkilling, or for some other reason. The crop is widely grown to a slight degree in the Rocky Mountain area, both as a dry land crop and under irrigation. Another center of barley production lies in the great interior valley of California (Figs. 36, 37). The one grown in the southern portion, the San Joaquin valley, is mostly used for livestock, while that of the northern portion, the Sacramento valley, is used for malting purposes. The crop is also widely grown throughout the United States as a temporary pasture crop.

TABLE 7.—*The Production of Barley (bushels) in Various States for 1945.*

North Dakota	53,760,000
California	41,608,000
South Dakota	32,900,000
Colorado	19,551,000
Nebraska	13,420,000
Montana	13,248,000
Minnesota	13,224,000
Idaho	11,840,000
Utah	6,750,000
Oregon	6,402,000
United States, total	263,961,000

The extensive distribution of barley culture over the northern hemisphere at once suggests that the crop is adapted to a wide variation of climatic and soil conditions. The situation recalls a similar relationship as to wheat and rye. While the entire geographical range of barley is truly remarkable, nevertheless, it is true, again as with wheat and corn, that the crop does best within a much more limited climatic and soil environment. We may readily distinguish certain centers of barley production (Fig. 36), that is "Barley Belts," just as we have pointed out for the wheat and corn belts. All of these belts are definitely correlated with climate, and to a somewhat less obvious degree with soils. In so far as climatic controls are concerned, barley has the great advantage over wheat that it matures in a shorter period. In this way

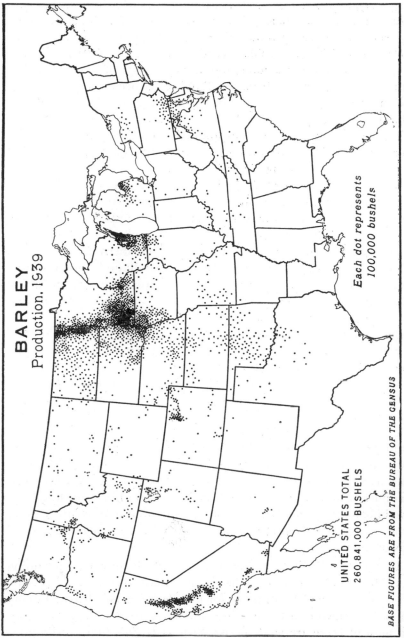

BARLEY
Production. 1939

UNITED STATES TOTAL
260,841,000 BUSHELS

BASE FIGURES ARE FROM THE BUREAU OF THE CENSUS

Each dot represents
100,000 bushels

FIG. 37. The production of barley in the United States in 1939. (Photo from Bureau of Agricultural Economics, U. S. Department of Agriculture.)

barley may, and often does, escape the dangers of aridity in low latitudes and altitudes. Barley is a cool-weather crop. The crop does
very well in the Rocky Mountains at 7,000 feet, in the Caucasus at
8,500, and in Tibet at 10,000 feet above sea level. One very hardy
variety is said to produce good crops at an altitude of 14,000 feet. Its
culture extends poleward from the Tropic of Cancer along the Middle
Nile and from northern India to or beyond the Arctic Circle in Russia
and Scandinavia.

The best conditions for the production of barley in the United
States are to be found from the northern portion of the corn belt and
northward, into the spring wheat belt (Fig. 36). It is also valuable in
parts of the hay and dairy region in the north and east. The moister
cooler climatic areas favor, in general, the production of barley for
malting purposes, while the warmer drier areas are better for the production of the harder types of barley for feeding purposes. The
cooler more humid climate of central and northern Europe favors
barley over wheat. The relatively cool and humid winter of the
Mediterranean type of climate favors the crop in southern Spain and
North Africa. The grain matures there before the onset of the hot and
dry weather of spring and summer.

Barley differs from wheat in its relationship to the soil; it does not
do well on the heavier clay soils of humid climates. This is because
good soil drainage and aeration are especially necessary for the health
of barley. Sandy soils are very unsatisfactory for barley, but it will
endure considerably higher concentration of soil alkali and soluble
salts than will either wheat or corn. If it were not for the fact that
barley is injured by hot humid weather the crop could be grown successfully in the deep, rich soils of the corn belt. Thus we see again
how climate and soil introduce significant combinations to which crop
plants as well as native grasses must become adapted if they are to be
economically successful. These natural relationships are deeply involved in all of our modern attempts to adjust and improve the culture
of the leading cereals to the natural conditions of the major grassland
areas of the world.

The generic distinction which marks all species of barley, including
the wild and cultivated forms, have come down to us from prehistoric
times. The original Latin name for the plant was *Hordeum*. Twenty
or more species of this genus are now recognized by agrostologists.
The most of these are wild species, such as *H. jubatum*, a wild grass
that is widely known as Squirrel-tail Grass or Foxtail Barley, and they

are mostly worthless or even troublesome weeds in many places throughout the world.

The wild barley grass, *Hordeum spontaneum* of western Asia, has been regarded as the ancestral species of our modern cultivated barleys. Early scientific investigators noted that some kinds of barley produce two rows of grain in the heads, and that others produce six rows in each head. This observation suggested the common types now recognized, namely, "two-rowed" barley and "six-rowed" barley. These characteristics are still recognized in the classification of the numerous varieties of cultivated barley, even though the latter differ in many other respects.

In modern times Linnaeus in 1748 and 1753 proposed a simple classification of barley that marks the beginning of all of the more or less complex schemes of classification that have been developed since that period. He established the genus *Hordeum* to include all kinds of barley then known, both the wild and the cultivated species and varieties. Linnaeus recognized two species of two-rowed barley, namely *H. distichon* and *H. zeocriton,* and two of the six-rowed type, *H. hexastichon* and *H. vulgare.* He also included one variety, a hull-less type, under each of the two groups of species.

A summary of Linnaeus' scheme of classification of cultivated barley as he understood it is shown in the following outline:

  I. SIX-ROWED BARLEY
    1. *Hordeum vulgare,* Hulled, lax, six-rowed barley
    2. *H. vulgare coeleste,* Hull-less, lax, six-rowed barley
    3. *Hordeum hexastichon,* Dense, hulled, six-rowed barley
  II. TWO-ROWED BARLEY
    1. *Hordeum distichon,* Hulled, lax, two-rowed barley
    2. *H. distichon nudum,* Hull-less, lax, two-rowed barley
    3. *Hordeum zeocriton,* Dense, hulled, two-rowed barley

There has been a strong tendency in late years to consider cultivated barley as a single species, called either *H. vulgare* or *H. sativum,* to assume that this species developed from the original wild barley, *H. spontaneum,* and that all modern cultivated varieties of barley originated from this one original cultigen. Still later work suggests that there may have been *two* ancestral wild species of barley from which there were four cultivated species originally developed. Four species commonly recognized today are *H. vulgare,* and *H. interme-*

dium, the six-rowed barleys, and *H. distichon* and *H. deficiens,* the two-rowed barleys. The scores of cultivated barleys that are now distinguished by agronomists are varieties of these four species. These numerous forms differ from each other upon various characteristics such as, whether the kernels are hulled or naked (hull-less), whether the lemmas are awned or hooded, color of scales and grain, early or late types, and many technical details. The methods of modern breeding continue to produce new varieties of barley without end, it would seem. More than forty new varieties have been released to the farmers of the United States in the last ten years. These have increased the yield from three to five bushels per acre over the varieties that they replaced.

Mankind grows barley today for two principal purposes: for feed for his livestock and for the preparation of malt and malt products. The barleys grown for feed are usually six-rowed varieties with rather hard grain. Those grown for malt are the larger, two-rowed forms with softer grain.

The grain of barley was used for bread in ancient and medieval times and it still is to a degree in certain northern areas and at higher elevations where it may be the only cereal grown. A deficiency of gluten makes barley flour a relatively poor breadstuff, nevertheless, unleavened barley cakes are still more or less popular in far northern regions. It is an important crop for man and beast where climatic conditions are too severe for wheat, rye, or corn. It is favored for livestock in the dry subtropical climate because it ripens in the short, cool, growing season during the low sun period that precedes the long, dry, season of summer. Winter barley makes a good pasture crop in many places. It is grown for such purposes on the Pacific coast and in the southeastern states, as well as in the central portion of the winter wheat area of the United States.

A special processing of the grain prepares barley for a number of uses, besides bread. "Pot barley" is made simply by milling off the husk from the kernels. If the surface of the husked kernels is ground still more, the "pearl barley" familiar in soups is produced. About two million bushels are used for these purposes.

Barley has long been the chief source of malt for alcoholic beverages. Barley wine and beer from barley were made in ancient times. Beer, made from barley, mostly in the Old World monasteries, was popular during the Middle Ages. From the relatively crude, home-made methods that produced the inferior but often highly intoxicating beverages of early times have come the greatly improved and highly technical processes that characterize the modern industry of malting and brewing, with its great variety of finished products.

Large quantities of barley are used in various countries for the production of malt in the brewing and distilling industry and for malt extracts for various purposes. The United States uses 75 million or more bushels of barley a year for fermented and distilled beverages.

The world production of beer in 1938 was about 200 million barrels. In 1940 the United States produced and distributed nearly 55 million barrels of malt liquors. This represented a sales value estimated at 1.8 million dollars.

Malt owes its value in the brewing industry to the abundance of a certain sugar, called maltose, which is produced by the digestion of the starch in the germinating barley grains. Maltose is sometimes substituted for glucose or grape sugar for other purposes. The Japanese prepare maltose by the fermentation of rice starch, from which they produce their famous beverage known as Sake. Sake contains a higher percentage of alcohol than do most beers and wines, and hence is commonly more intoxicating.

CHAPTER 7

Oats

IF WE SELECTED OUR FOODS FOR THEIR NUTRITIVE QUALITIES ALONE, oats would be more popular as human food. The grain of oats is rich in fats, proteins, and minerals, as well as in carbohydrates and vitamins, and on the whole it supplies the best balanced and most nutritious food of all the cereals. The low gluten content of oat dough renders it unsuitable for making of popular light bread, but oatmeal cakes and rolled oats are among nature's finest and most easily prepared natural foods for man. In spite of these well-known facts mankind the world over still insists that oats are good only for horses and other animals. The famous English writer of the eighteenth century, Samuel Johnson, defined oats as food for men in Scotland, horses in England. The canny Scots replied to this quip that England was noted for the excellence of her horses, Scotland for the excellence of her men. Nutritionists, farmers, and other influential folks should introduce some popular song or radio program that would din into ears the superior value of oats as food for *man,* as well as for mares.

Oats have not been cultivated as long as have wheat and barley. The crop seems to have been unknown to the most ancient Asiatic civilizations. The plant was regarded either as a worthless weed or useful only as a medicinal plant by such ancient Roman and Greek writers on agriculture as Cato, Varro, and Theophrastus. It is probable that the common oat, from which most cultivated varieties have been developed, originated in Asia Minor and appeared first as a weed in the grain fields of Greece and Rome. Oats were more or less popular as food for man in later Greece, and somewhat later still among the Germanic tribes of the west and north at about the beginning of the Christian era. The Slavic people of eastern Europe apparently cultivated oats during the Bronze and Iron Ages. Porridge made from oats became popular for human consumption in the early years of the

British Isles. This is still an important food in Scotland and Ireland and the islands to the north. Seed oats marched along with the other small grains when the American colonists set up their homes on our eastern seaboard in the early seventeenth century (Fig. 38).

The distribution of oat culture across the modern world follows more or less generally, as one would expect, the pattern set by the great natural grasslands, and by the cultivation of the other cereals that are at home in the intermediate types of climate. The global distribution of oats most nearly resembles that of rye. This is especially noteworthy for the Old World where the maps for oats and rye might almost be interchanged, except for the important fact that rye culture marches appreciably farther poleward. Oats are much more important than rye in the western world, however, and are much more widely distributed in North America than is rye. Both Canada and the United States are

FIG. 38. The oat plant (wild oats) showing portions of the stem, leaves, cluster of spikelets (panicle), a spikelet, and a single floret *(from Hitchcock).*

prominent growers of this crop (Fig. 39). Oats are relatively unimportant in the southern hemisphere, although the crop is grown to a minor degree in Argentina, Australia, and New Zealand. The more important features of the geographical distribution of oats in the modern world are shown in the following outline:

I. NORTHERN AND NORTHWESTERN EUROPE
    1. Poland, Germany, Sweden, France
    2. Denmark, Great Britain

II. RUSSIA AND ROMANIA

III. NORTH AMERICA
    1. United States
    2. Canada

IV. SOUTH AMERICA

The annual production of oats in the world reaches the enormous total of about 4,250,000,000 bushels (Table 8). The mild, cool, humid climate of northwestern Europe and the flexibility of oats as to its demands on the soil are the principal features that contribute to the notable success of the crop in that region. The demand for oats for livestock is also great throughout that area, and this greatly intensifies the importance of the oat crop there.

The highest yields per acre of oats in the world are commonly secured in Denmark, Great Britain, Sweden, France, and Germany. Germany normally produces about 550 million bushels on 8 million acres, France 325 million bushels on 8.3 million acres, but production in these countries is now low. Great Britain produces 227 million bushels on 3.3 million acres, Sweden 78 million bushels on 1.6 million acres, and Denmark about 68.5 million bushels on 0.95 million acres, with the highest yield of all at about 72 bushels per acre. On the heavier, better soils of certain parts of Germany oats tend to give way to barley as the major feed crop, but wherever the soil is sandy oats are likely to prevail.

TABLE 8.—*The Production of Oats (bushels) in Various Countries and the World, for 1945 except as otherwise noted.*

United States	1,547,663,000
Russia (1930–1934)	936,735,000
Germany (1935–1939)	405,335,000
Canada	381,596,000
United Kingdom	227,150,000
Poland (1935–1939)	180,741,000
France	172,000,000
Denmark	68,205,000
Argentina	54,881,000
Sweden	54,309,000
Romania (1930–1934)	52,899,000
Australia and New Zealand	26,625,000
World, total	4,250,000,000

Poland also is included in the great oat belt that is roughly centered on the parallel of 50° North and across northern Europe from that country to France and Britain. Poland, as we think of it before the beginning of World War II, produced about 180 million bushels of oats annually on about 5.4 million acres.

The north European oat belt stretches eastward to about 60° East longitude in the form of a narrow tongue across the great grassland

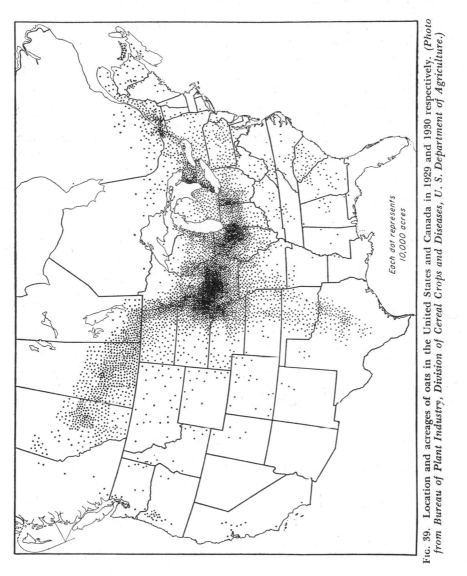

Fig. 39. Location and acreages of oats in the United States and Canada in 1929 and 1930 respectively. (Photo from Bureau of Plant Industry, Division of Cereal Crops and Diseases, U. S. Department of Agriculture.)

Each dot represents 10,000 acres

plains of Russia. The crop does best in the U.S.S.R. in the less arid zone somewhat to the north of the centers of wheat and barley production. It is of importance well northward of the steppe lands proper and into the southern reaches of the great subpolar forest or taiga of the Russian Union. Oats are grown also, but with diminishing importance, far to the eastward from the above Russian center to the region of Lake Baikal and on beyond the Yablonovoi Ridge to the valley of the Amur River. Some oats are also grown as far east as in Korea, and Hokkaido, northern Japan. In Russia the yield of oats is only about 24 bushels per acre, but the vast acreage (about 42 million acres) returns a crop of approximately 1,000,000,000 bushels per year, about 25 per cent of the world's total production of oats.

Romania and the Balkan states grow oats too, but those areas are really outside the main oat belt of Europe. The annual production in Romania is around 53 million bushels on a little more than two million acres.

There is an oat belt as well developed in the United States and Canada as in Europe. Its center (Fig. 39) is along a curved strip extending from Ontario, western New York and Pennsylvania, westward to northern Ohio, across Indiana, central Illinois, Iowa, northeastern Nebraska, southern Minnesota, eastern Dakota, and into southern Manitoba and Saskatchewan. Lobes of this main oat belt extend southward into Kansas, Oklahoma and Texas, and into Michigan where production is important. Outlying areas of production also are found in the southeastern states, in the irrigated sections of the plains states, and in Washington, Oregon, and California. In general, the principal oat belt of the United States coincides with the corn belt. As a feed crop, oats is of great importance across the northern part of the corn area. Spring oats are often sown on land that was in corn the previous year in that area. Winter oats are commonly grown in the southern states and in the states of the west coast.

TABLE 9.—*The Production of Oats (bushels) in Various States for 1945.*

Minnesota	155,960,000
Iowa	135,198,000
Wisconsin	118,938,000
Illinois	100,896,000
South Dakota	92,430,000
North Dakota	82,041,000
Michigan	44,100,000
Texas	38,600,000
Nebraska	35,586,000
Missouri	29,970,000
United States, total	1,154,666,000

The United States (Fig. 40) annually produces from 900,000,000 bushels to over 1,540 million bushels of oats on 35 million to 40 million acres, with an average yield of about 26 bushels per acre (Table 9). We commonly rank second to Russia in quantity of oats grown. Iowa, Minnesota, and Illinois commonly lead the states in the total yield of oats. Canada produces 350 million to 400 million bushels on about 13 million acres, and commonly ranks fourth among the nations in production.

The cool, humid climate of extreme southwestern Australia, Tasmania, and New Zealand favors oat production. Seventeen million to twenty-four million bushels are grown in that region as a whole. The only important areas of South Africa where oats are grown coincide with the areas of rich dark soils and native tall-grass prairies of Orange Free State and the Transvaal. About 8 million bushels per year is the oat production there.

The important cereal center of the Argentinian pampa is also the area of greatest oat production in the southern hemisphere. About 65 million bushels per year is the output of that region. Oats are grown there toward the southern portion of the wheat crescent (Fig. 16) especially in the cooler southeastern part of the wheat area as a whole. Oats are grown in Argentina also for winter forage to supplement other pasturage. Chile also grows about five million bushels which are distributed through the great central valley.

These statements serve to recall that oats is another valuable cereal whose main geographical distribution closely parallels the great grasslands of the northern hemisphere. Of all the cereals whose production shows this relationship to the areas of native vegetation with their grasses, soils, and climate, wheat is of course the most outstanding in the degree of perfection of its adaptation to the natural grassland environment.

Oats, like rye, do best in the cool humid variations of the intermediate climates. Their centers of greatest production are, therefore, somewhat poleward from the major centers of wheat production in the Old World, and somewhat eastward and northward from the great wheat-growing region of the United States. Oats are better adapted to the woodland (savanna-woodland) type of intermediate climates than to the steppe or prairie climates. They are somewhat more sensitive to cold, because of their longer season, than rye and barley, and therefore less successful at the higher latitudes and altitudes. Certain varieties of oats, red oats, especially, are used with success, however, in warmer, drier climates. These varieties have a naturally shorter growing season, so that when sown in the fall they mature before the hot, dry weather of the following early summer injures the crop. On account of these relationships such varieties are sparingly grown in the dry lands of South Africa, North Africa, and the winter wheat regions of our own Great Plains.

Oats are not particularly exacting as to their soil requirements. They do best on soils that are firm, loamy and moist. They do well even on cool, sandy soils if there is plenty of water present. Oats do well on cold, sandy soils, too, and thus are sometimes seen at high latitudes along with rye and barley. The short-season varieties, when sown as winter oats are fairly successful in the drier, warmer soils outside the main oat belts. The crop responds in a notable manner to irrigation and to the application of fertilizers when carefully managed.

The word *Avena* has been applied to oats in a more or less generic sense since ancient times. Pliny wrote of *Avena graeca,* the Greek Oat. Numerous species of *wild* oats have been known for centuries. Among these are *Avena fatua* and *A. sterilis.* The latter and the derived and cultivated Red Oat, *A. byzantina,* have been known and grown in the Mediterranean region for many centuries, as has *A. abyssinica* in the Ethiopian highlands. Varieties of the European Red Oat are widely grown with success in the warm, dry intermediate climates of the world. The Common Cultivated Oat, *Avena sativa,* and the Side Oat, *A. orientalis,* are thought to have been derived from the Wild Oat, *A. fatua,* of the Old World. Another wild oat of the European area is *A. barbata,* from which *A. brevis,* the Short Oat, and *A. strigosa,* the Hairy Oat have developed. The interesting *A. nuda,* a Hull-less or Naked Oat is a species from central Asia.

Some of the more common or important species of oats that have been recognized are summarized in the following list:

> Common or White Oats, *A. sativa*
> Side Oats, *A. orientalis*
> Common Wild Oats, *A. fatua*
> Red Oats, *A. byzantina*
> Short Oats, *A. brevis*
> Arid Wild Oats, *A. sterilis*
> Hull-less or Naked Oats, *A. nuda*
> Hairy Oats, *A. strigosa*
> Slender Wild Oats, *A. barbata*

The old word *Avena* was established in 1700 as the proper generic name for oats by the great French botanist Tournefort, the author of

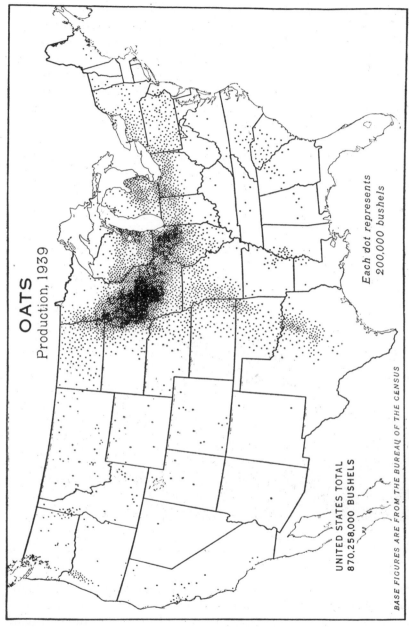

OATS
Production, 1939

UNITED STATES TOTAL
870,258,000 BUSHELS

*Each dot represents
200,000 bushels*

BASE FIGURES ARE FROM THE BUREAU OF THE CENSUS

FIG. 40. The production of oats in the United States for 193 9. *(Photo from Bureau of Agricultural Economics, U. S. Department of Agriculture.)*

many genera of plants. Linnaeus accepted this name in 1753 as the rightful generic name for all oats. Most of the hundreds of cultivated kinds of oats that are known today are varieties or strains of the Common Oat, *A. sativa*, the Red Oat, *A. byzantina,* or the Side Oat, *A. orientalis.* Many of our American and Canadian oats may be traced to original importations from the Old World, especially from Russia. Such variety names as Kherson, Green Russian, Tartar, and Tobolsk reflect their Russian derivation.

Fig. 41. An example of large-scale grain harvesting by means of combine drawn by a caterpillar Diesel tractor. *(Photo from near Fenn, Idaho; furnished by Caterpillar Tractor Co.)*

Spring oats and winter oats, and types of these that are suitable to or preferable for certain climatic and soil variations and uses, have been and are being developed and improved by breeding and selection throughout the world. Three hundred or more of such forms have been recognized and the oat breeders continue their important work.

A variety that is known as "Cedar Oats" has recently been perfected for use in Nebraska.

Only a small proportion of the enormous oat crop of the world is used as food for man. Oatmeal is a food that is rich in fats, proteins, minerals, and vitamins, as well as high in its energy-yielding capacity from its abundant carbohydrates. Oatmeal cakes, biscuits, and rolled oats are very popular among the outdoor people of northern lands, and to a less degree as breakfast food throughout the world. About three per cent of the oat crop of the United States is used for human food.

As a food for livestock oats are used in two principal forms namely, the grain and the green fodder or forage. The nutritious grain has long been an important leading stock food, especially for horses. Ground oats are used in combination with other grain feeds for poultry and other livestock. Most of the oats grown are used in the localities where they are produced, especially in the great centers of livestock production.

Oats are of wide value also as green forage and hay for livestock, including dairy cattle, especially in those areas where winter oats do well. The Wild Oats, *A. fatua* and *A. barbata,* often furnish much hay either in the wild form or as cultivated crops. Much oat straw, the most nutritious of all small grain straw after threshing, is also fed to livestock. Oats are often sown as a nurse crop, that is, with such crops as alfalfa, because of the protective value it gives the young delicate seedlings of the primary crop during the first season. Another important value of oats in a scientific scheme of farm management is that the crop is a fine one to alternate with corn, especially where the production of large numbers of livestock, as in the corn belt, favors such a rotation.

CHAPTER 8

Rye

RYE IS THE MOST ADAPTABLE OF ALL THE CEREALS, BUT ITS MARCH across the world has been attended by much uncertainty and counter propaganda when it has been urged as a human food. It holds its place only as the approved second choice for light bread in the face of the age-old competition with wheat, the master cereal for light bread. Rye bread was popular in Europe during the Middle Ages in spite of the efforts to glorify wheat as the only "noble" bread for master men. It became the widely accepted choice in Germany, Poland, and Russia. As late as 1700 this heavy "evil smelling" grain was used for as much as forty per cent of the bread of England. The better rising quality and the lightness of wheat bread, coupled with better transportation facilities, continued to rule against rye so that in 1800 rye bread was scarcely known in England except as a novelty. Rye has never been completely displanted, however, and today it is used for bread in large quantities in Russia, Poland, Germany, and the Baltic States.

Rye produces grain second in popularity only to wheat for the making of light bread. The flour made from the slim, elongated kernels of rye produces a fair supply of gluten, thus the dough may be raised by the use of yeast. Rye has been used for bread for centuries and it is still an important bread crop in Scandinavia, Finland, Russia, and Germany, but on the whole rye seems to become less and less important for such purposes, especially wherever wheat flour can be secured.

Rye appears to be of much more recent origin than either wheat or barley. It is not referred to in the records of ancient Chinese or Japanese agriculture, and it has not been found in any of the monuments of the ancient Egyptian civilization or the Lake Dwellings of Europe. It was known, however, to the early Greeks and Romans. Rye is probably a native of the region of the Caspian and Black seas

102

of southwestern Russia where it is said to have been first cultivated. It spread from that area to the north and west where promptly it became an important source of fairly light bread for the Slavic people of southeastern Europe. Finally, the Germanic people of western and

northern Europe adopted rye as their major bread crop. Rye for bread was a very important crop during colonial times in America and until after the Revolutionary War. The growing popularity of wheat and its increasing accessibility the world round, especially with the westward expansion of agriculture in the United States, early tended to reduce the use of rye for bread-making purposes and to increase wheat consumption for that basic demand.

Unlike other cereals, rye has not become the important crop in the distant reaches of the world far from its original center. It is scarcely known in the southern hemisphere except slightly in South Africa, southeastern Australia, eastern New Zealand, Argentina, and the central valley of

Fig. 42. The rye plant showing portions of stem, leaves, head, spikelet, and single floret *(from Hitchcock).*

Chile. In the north it is still an outstanding crop in northern Europe and central Russia.

The rye belt of the Old World marches from northern France and Belgium eastward across Europe and far into Russia. It thinly extends itself as a long, slender, broken strip that rambles eastward over the steppes and arid lands of southern Siberia to Manchuria. There is also an isolated area of rye production in the arid western lands of the Kizil Kum plain southeast of the Aral Sea. The general belt is bordered by less important producing areas that extend northward to the Arctic Circle and westward to Turkey, North Africa, and Spain.

The production of rye in the United States was formerly centered in Pennsylvania, Michigan, Wisconsin, and Minnesota (Figs. 43, 44). More recently, however, the crop became of increasing importance in the Dakotas and Nebraska. From these better established centers the crop has thinly fanned southward and eastward into the corn belt and westward into the northern Great Plains of the United States and Canada. Winter rye is successful in the latter area even under the rather severe climatic conditions that exist there. The well-known drought resistance of rye favors its increasing production in the central Great Plains area. Little rye is grown in the states of the Pacific Coast.

TABLE 10.—*The Production of Rye (bushels) in Various Countries and the World, for 1945 except as otherwise noted.*

Russia (1930–1934)		829,024,000
Germany (1943)		300,967,000
Poland (1935–1939)		263,787,000
France (1935–1939)		30,013,000
United States		26,354,000
Hungary (1944)		25,000,000
Lithuania (1935–1939)		24,691,000
Spain		22,000,000
Belgium (1943)		13,063,000
Sweden (1943)		16,000,000
Netherlands, Latvia, Finland, Romania, each	9 to	15,000,000
Canada		5,888,000
World, total		1,550,000,000

The annual world production of rye amounts to about 1,550,000,000 bushels, on about 112 million acres (Table 10). Fully nine-tenths of the world's crop is grown in the great European and Russian rye belt. Russia commonly leads the world in rye production, the annual crop there amounting to about 830 million bushels on 65 million acres. Germany is next with 300 million bushels on 15 million acres. Poland produces 265 million bushels, France 30 million, Hungary 26 million, Lithuania 24 million, Belgium, normally about 20 million but only 13 million in 1943, Sweden 16 million, and the Netherlands, Latvia, Finland, and Romania, produce from 9 to 15 million bushels each.

The total annual production of rye in the United States ranges from about 30 million to 55 million bushels on 2.5 million to 3 million acres (Table 11). Over the ten-year period from 1928 to 1937 North Dakota led the states in rye production with an average of 8 million bushels on 812 thousand acres. That state was followed in order by Minnesota, South Dakota, Nebraska, and Wisconsin. The total annual average for the United States for the same period was 36,300,000 bushels on 3,179,000 acres. Canada grows 5 to 9 million bushels of rye on 850 thousand acres.

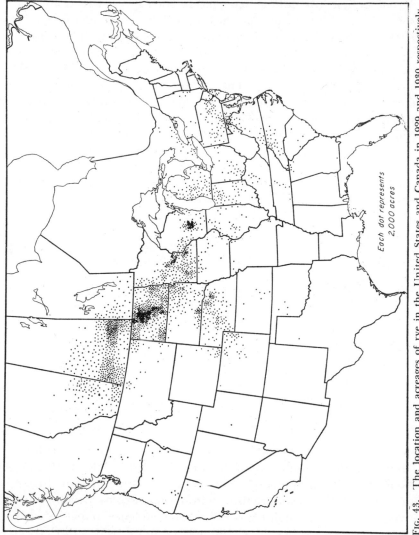

Each dot represents
2,000 acres

FIG. 43. The location and acreages of rye in the United States and Canada in 1929 and 1930 respectively. *(Photo from Bureau of Plant Industry, Division of Cereal Crops and Diseases, U. S. Department of Agriculture.)*

Rye does best in a mild climate and in good soils. Rye is unique, however, in its ability to produce at least a light crop under a greater variety of unfavorable conditions than any other cereal. The winter-hardy varieties of rye will endure more severe cold than any other cereal, and so they may be grown at higher latitudes and higher altitudes than barley or wheat. The rye belt of Europe is somewhat farther north than the farthermost northern extension of the wheat belt of Russia. The rye-growing areas of northwestern Europe lie within the influence of the mild humid winters and mild summers of the west coast marine type of intermediate climates. In the United States the area of greatest rye production lies to the north and west of the corn belt (Figs. 43, 44) and actually more or less overlaps the northern spring wheat belt in the Great Plains area. This area, as well as the Russian rye belt, is marked by the long, cold winters and short, warm summers of the intermediate types of climate.

TABLE 11.—*The Production of Rye (bushels) in Various States for 1945.*

South Dakota	4,495,000
Nebraska	4,472,000
North Dakota	2,418,000
Minnesota	1,815,000
Wisconsin	1,261,000
Indiana	1,112,000
Oklahoma	1,064,000
Michigan	900,000
Kansas	788,000
Colorado	780,000
United States, total	26,354,000

Some of the out-lying areas of minor importance for rye culture are found within the influence of the extensive arid and desert climates of Asia. The wide and fair success of rye in the latter types of climate illustrates its ability to endure the conditions imposed by low humidity, low soil moisture, and high temperature. Its tendency to mature early in such situations classifies it as a drought-escaping crop, a distinction which it shares, more or less, with barley. Rye sometimes becomes objectionable under dry-land conditions when it is allowed to contaminate winter wheat.

Rye is noteworthy also because it does well under a great variety of soil conditions. It is perhaps the least fastidious of all the cereals in its soil requirements. It prefers good drainage and good soils, but it does very well on the poor, damp, cold, sandy, and peaty soils of

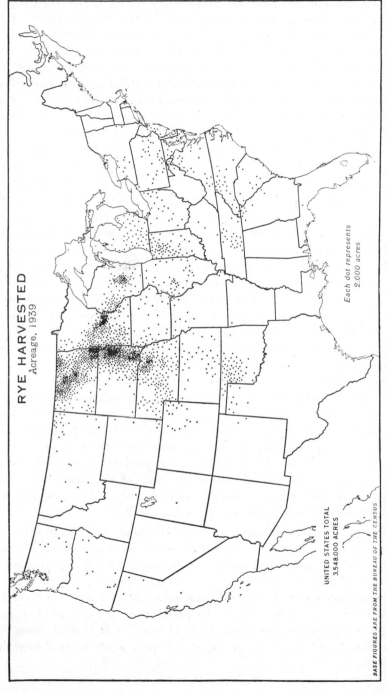

RYE HARVESTED
Acreage, 1939

Each dot represents
2,000 acres

UNITED STATES TOTAL
3,548,000 ACRES

BASE FIGURES ARE FROM THE BUREAU OF THE CENSUS

FIG. 44. The location and acreages of rye in the United States in 1959. (*Photo from Bureau of Agricultural Economics, U. S. Department of Agriculture.*)

western and northern Europe. The yields per acre are even rather high in that region. It will endure considerable soil alkalinity. But, of course, rye does best in the good deep, rich soils of the Ukraine and central Russia and on the northern prairies of the United States. Rye will continue to produce on rather poor soils longer than any of the other cereals. Rye is a good example of a cultivated grass that is very important in areas where subsistence agriculture demands a hardy crop.

Cultivated rye belongs to the same major group or tribe of grasses as do wheat and barley. All of the domesticated varieties of rye are commonly included under the single species, *Secale cereale*. This species probably originated from a wild relative, *Secale anatolicum,* which grows wild today in the arid wastes of Asia Minor, Armenia, Iran, and the Kirghiz steppes. Certain students of the evolution of the cereals hold, on the other hand, that the original wild ancestor of our modern rye was a different species, *Secale montanum,* which grows in Europe and Asia. Only a few varieties of cultivated rye are now recognized.

Flour made from rye makes good, but rather heavy, damp bread that has been popular for centuries and is still used in large quantities in Germany, Russia, Finland, and Scandinavia. Rye bread became very popular in Germany early in World War II. Nazi leaders knew full well that the war would soon cut off all imports of wheat, so their powerful propaganda stressed the absolute need for an expansion of the use of rye bread by playing up its supposedly superior qualities as compared with wheat. Nevertheless, rye bread is commonly second choice for most people if wheat bread is available at the same price. The heavy, close-grained, dark bread, the *Schwartzbrot,* of those northern lands is made from rye. Such bread has good keeping qualities. Rye flour and wheat flour are usually mixed in various proportions in making the so-called rye breads that are used on a relatively small scale in the United States. These are more of the nature of snacks rather than regular major foods in our country, even when they are made of as much as seventy per cent wheat flour.

Rye makes excellent livestock food. Ground rye and rye bran are used extensively for cattle, sheep, and swine. It is also grown for pasturage and hay, as a green manure crop, and as a cover crop to control erosion. Winter rye is valuable as a forage crop in the fall and early spring in those climates that are characterized by early summer drought.

Rye has long been used in the production of malt, alcohol, and spiritous liquors, such as gin and rye whiskey. Gin is made from rye in Holland and the *kvass* of the Russians is made from this grain.

Several million bushels of rye are used for these purposes each year.

The long uniform straw of the rye plant is used, among others for packing materials, mattresses, hats, paper, shoes, and mats.

Thus we see that rye, although a minor cereal, marches with the life of mankind at many widely separated points and for many important reasons. It has a real place in the economy of the world, and is deserving of much wider cultivation and use in the western hemisphere.

CHAPTER 9

The Sorghums and Millets

WE HAVE ALREADY POINTED OUT THAT VARIOUS CEREALS ARE CHAR-
acteristic of certain agricultural civilizations that were originally centered in fairly well-defined regions of the globe. The "grand march"
of these dominant masters of man's destiny has led each of these types
of true grasses outward from their respective places of origin to world-
encircling acclaim. The original centers of the sorghums and millets
were in central India, northern China and in,the tropical African
savannas. These grasses have been of utmost value for several millenia as contributors of human food within the lands of their origin.
They have never become of much importance as cereals for direct
human consumption outside those natal lands, but they are of great
value in connection with the production of livestock and for other
uses, in the New World as well as the Old.

Sorghums and millets are among the very oldest of the important
cultivated plants known to man. They include many true grasses that
present a great variety of characteristics and values. Certain of these
coarse grasses have been widely grown for centuries. They have
played an important role in the history of civilization and in the outward march of agriculture across the globe from earliest times. Archi-
tectural designs in which sorghum was depicted have been found in
the tombs of Egypt that date as early at 2,200 B.C. Many archaeological and linguistic studies serve to trace them far back in the history
of Egypt, Syria, and Mesopotamia. The widespread cultivation and
importance of these hardy grasses in ancient times are thoroughly
attested to by records from the Nile, the irrigated farms of Babylon,
India, China, and Italy. The ancient caravans that threaded their
slow courses across the dreary wastes that mark the cradle of mankind
carried these life-giving grasses throughout the then-known world.
India, China, and Africa have apparently been the centers of origin

110

of many of our latter-day varieties of cultivated sorghums. The sorghums and millets occupy an increasingly important place in the complex picture of the agricultural interests of the world today. They are widely grown for grain and forage, especially in the New World. They are very important sources of human food in the Old World, especially in Africa, India, and China.

FIG. 45. Dakota Amber Sorgo. An early, drought-resistant variety; good for the short season and limited rainfall of the Northern Great Plains section of the United States. *(Photo from Bureau of Plant Industry, Division of Cereal Crops and Diseases, U. S. Department of Agriculture.)*

Sorghums, especially broomcorn, and millets, marched to America with the early colonists from Europe, but it is apparent that these grasses were of slight importance during colonial times. They are said to have reached the West Indies from Africa along with the importation of Negro slaves. Cultivation of the sorghums in America seriously began about 1850–1860. Chinese varieties of sorghum were brought to the United States about that time. From that period the spread of sorghum culture in this country has been steady and important. The vigorous march of settlers into the less humid and the semiarid lands of our country that lie in the vast Trans-Mississippi region was followed by an increasing introduction, popularity, and success of the sorghums. A real sorghum belt (Figs. 46, 47, 48) has been developed in the West since 1890. The recurrent droughts to which our Great Plains are subject serve to maintain a lively interest in these valuable drought-resistant crops. It is truly an amazing sight to see a fine field of fresh, green, headed sorghum alongside a field of corn or wheat that has dried out and perished under the influence of extremely dry weather.

The sorghums and millets, like maize, wheat, and oats can now be said to be truly *global* in their distribution, but of major importance mainly in the northern hemisphere. The principal centers of production of these versatile grasses are northern China, Manchuria, India, Afghanistan, southeastern Europe and southern Russia, North Africa, Egypt, the African Savannas, and the Great Plains of North America. To a much smaller degree they are also grown in Central America, South America, and Australia.

The North China area produces about 14 million tons of millet per year, much of which is for human food. This is especially valuable in places where rice and corn are practically absent. The yield of millet is exceeded only by wheat in that area which embraces much of the provinces of Shansi, Shensi, Kansu, Hopei, and Shantung. Considerable quantities of sorghum and millet are also grown in Japan, Borneo, and southeastern Australia, but reliable statistics are not available for those regions. Japan is reported to produce about 35 million bushels of millet annually, the most of which is probably used for human consumption.

The millets and sorghums are probably of more importance in India and Africa than anywhere else in the world. These crops are extensively grown throughout the western half of the Deccan, and northward toward the Himalayas. They are grown in the arid lands of Rajputana and the Punjab, and on into Baluchistan and Afghanistan. More than 500 million bushels are grown in this immense area. These crops, especially the sorghums, are grown throughout that region very largely for human food. Both spring and winter varieties of the crops are involved, and vigorous efforts are made to adjust the crops to the severe climatic and soil conditions that prevail over those relatively barren lands.

The widely scattered regions of sorghum culture in Africa are of great importance also, since the native populations of such areas use the grain for food. Many of these areas are located in the general belt

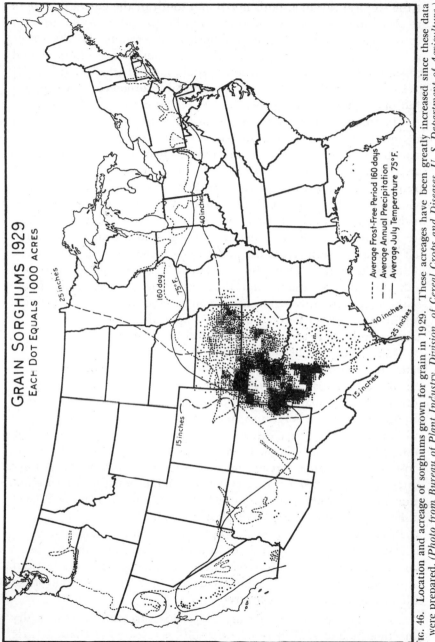

GRAIN SORGHUMS 1929
EACH DOT EQUALS 1000 ACRES

Average Frost-Free Period 160 days
Average Annual Precipitation
Average July Temperature 75°F.

Fig. 46. Location and acreage of sorghums grown for grain in 1929. These acreages have been greatly increased since these data were prepared. (*Photo from Bureau of Plant Industry, Division of Cereal Crops and Diseases, U. S. Department of Agriculture.*)

of the tropical savanna, both north and south of the equator. There are also important areas of production in Egypt and in dry subtropical North Africa. About 50 million bushels of sorghum on the whole are produced in the "dark" continent. Southeastern Europe and Russia produce about 140 million bushels, most of which is grown for livestock rather than for man. Considerable broomcorn, which is a kind of sorghum, is also grown in the Balkan States and in Italy.

The sorghums have been grown in the United States for less than one hundred years. During the past fifty years intensive and extensive trials have shown that they really have a place in American agriculture. They are especially valuable in the semiarid and arid regions to the west and southwest of the corn belt. Their noteworthy success, especially of the grain sorghums under severe drought, has resulted in their extension over a wide area of the Great Plains region. The sweet (forage) sorghums do better in the humid region of the cotton belt of the southern states, but these too are grown with some success in the arid lands. There is a well-defined sorghum belt including both the grain sorghums and the sweet (forage) sorghums, in the southern Great Plains region from Kansas to southwest Texas. Grain sorghums have also become of local importance under irrigation in Arizona and in the central valley of California.

Texas, with a yield of about 96 million bushels in 1944, leads the states in the production of grain sorghums. Kansas produced 49 million bushels in 1944, and other important but much lower yields are grown in Oklahoma, Colorado, Nebraska, and California. The total production of grain sorghums in the United States for 1944 was 181 million bushels, of dry, forage sorghums 12.3 million tons, and of ensilage (green) 6.3 million tons. One would expect a more or less constantly increasing acreage devoted to these crops in the United States in the immediate future. The total production of sorghum grain in the United States from 1936 to 1945 ranged from 30,270,000 bushels (1936) to 181,542,000 bushels in 1944.

Broomcorn, also a variety of sorghum, is grown on an intense scale in east central Illinois, south central Oklahoma, and the region of the Oklahoma panhandle, southwestern Kansas, and southeastern Colorado. These three sections include a total area of broomcorn in cultivation of about 300,000 acres.

The sorghums and millets are crops that successfully grow in dry, hot climates and also in rather dry soils. These vital characteristics naturally equip certain varieties of these crops to widespread culture

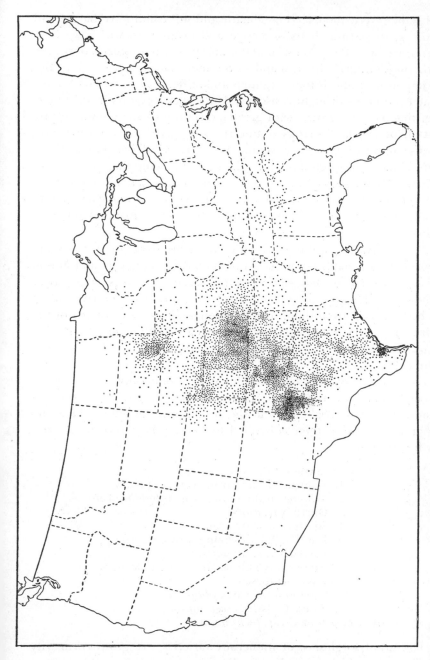

Fig. 47. The distribution and acreage of sorghums harvested for forage in 1934. Each dot represents 2,000 acres. *(Photo from Bureau of Plant Industry, Division of Cereal Crops and Diseases, U. S. Department of Agriculture.)*

under the severe and exacting climatic and soil conditions that prevail
in the great natural belts of steppe and savanna to which we have
often referred. They do much better and yield high returns, of course,
in the more humid climates and in the more moist, fertile soils. But
the important point is that sorghums and millets are possessed of much
greater powers of drought resistance than either corn or wheat. Therefore, they may be grown with greater certainty of success where production of the latter crops is uncertain or perennially unsuccessful
because of aridity. These simple facts clearly define the environmental place of sorghums and millets in the cropping program of
nations. Here again we find certain peculiar grasses that are possessed
of a very definite set of valuable characteristics and that yield a very
important series of products of outstanding value to mankind from
earliest times to the present.

The cultivated sorghums, of which there are scores of varieties, are
derived from a wild, perennial grass, known to botanists as Johnson
Grass, *Andropogon halepensis*. This variable wild species grows
naturally in the tropical and subtropical regions of the Old World. It
has been carried from those regions throughout the warm parts of the
globe. The cultivated varieties are known as *Sorghum vulgare, Andropogon sorghum,* or *Holcus sorghum, S. vulgare* being the preferred
technical name.

Four groups of cultivated sorghums are commonly recognized in
practice. They are the Grain Sorghums, the "Sorgos" or Sweet Sorghums, the Grass Sorghums, and the Broomcorn Sorghums. These together with some of their cultivated forms may be shown by the following grouping:

    I. THE GRAIN SORGHUMS
        1. Kafir or "Kafir Corn," var. *caffrorum*
        2. Milo or "milo maize," var. *subglabrescens*
        3. Durra, var. *durra*
        4. Shallu, var. *roxburghii*
        5. Kaoliang or Kowliang, var. *nervosum*
        6. Feterita, var. *caudatum*
    II. THE SORGOS OR SWEET SORGHUMS, var. *saccharatum*
    III. THE GRASS SORGHUMS
        1. Sudan Grass, var. *sudanense*
        2. Tunis Grass, *S. virgatum*
    IV. BROOMCORN, var. *technicum*

The grain sorghums, of numerous varieties, are grown primarily
for the grain which is used as food for man and beast. These have

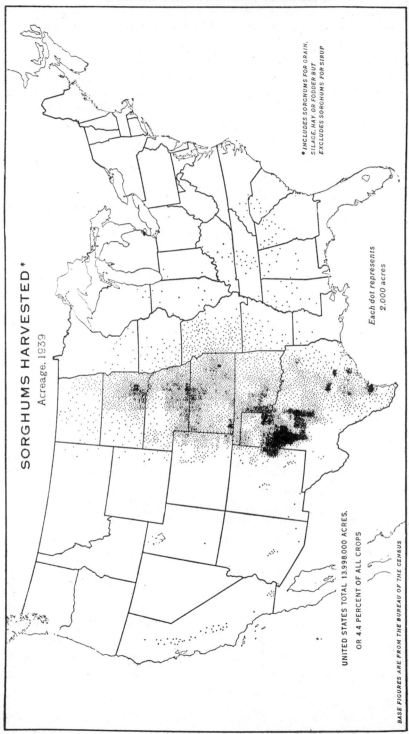

SORGHUMS HARVESTED *
Acreage, 1939

* INCLUDES SORGHUMS FOR GRAIN,
SILAGE, HAY OR FODDER BUT
EXCLUDES SORGHUMS FOR SIRUP

Each dot represents
2,000 acres

UNITED STATES TOTAL 13,998,000 ACRES,
OR 4.4 PERCENT OF ALL CROPS

BASE FIGURES ARE FROM THE BUREAU OF THE CENSUS

FIG. 48. Location and acreages of sorghums grown for grain, forage, hay, and fodder in 1939. (Photo from Bureau of Agricultural Economics, U. S. Department of Agriculture.)

furnished staple foods for mankind in the Old World for many centuries, especially in India, China, Japan, Asia Minor, and Africa. The grain is ground into flour from which bread, cakes and other types of food are made. Certain varieties of the grain sorghums that are valuable in the United States have been introduced from India and Africa. They are used here, both the grain and stover, for livestock. They are of great value to the farmers of the dry prairies and arid plains where corn and other grains and fodder crops are difficult to grow. Milo has been particularly good from southwestern Kansas to central Texas, and Kafir from eastern Kansas to western Oklahoma and the panhandle of Texas. Both of these varieties are from Africa. A variety of grain sorghum known as "Leoti" has recently been suggested for intensive culture in the United States as a possible source of starch to be substituted for cassava starch in the preparation of tapioca. Tapioca has been prepared exclusively from the root of a tropical plant known as *cassava* or *manioc,* chiefly from Brazil and the East Indies.

The Sorgos or Sweet Sorghums, *S. vulgare,* var. *saccharatum,* are usually tall, leafy plants that produce an abundance of sugar in their stems and leaves. These were brought to America from China and Africa. They are used for forage and silage, and sugar is also secured from their sap. They are grown in the more humid regions, especially for the syrup or "sorghum" that is made from the sap extracted from their stems. About 15 million gallons of sorghum syrup are annually made in the United States from the sorgos. A variety of sorgo that is known as Guinea Corn has long been grown as a source of sugar in China.

The forage sorghums are grown as pasture grasses and for hay. The principal variety concerned in the United States is commonly known as Sudan Grass, thus reflecting its African origin. This is a tall, erect, leafy, annual grass, that reaches heights of five to ten feet, depending upon conditions under which it is grown. It was introduced into the United States about 1909 and since that time it has been widely grown with success, particularly in the semiarid portions of the Great Plains, as well as in the humid southeastern states. It does well under irrigation and in a variety of soils, and is very drought-resistant. The relatively fine stems and abundant foliage are excellent for forage as in summer pastures and, when cured, they make good hay.

Broomcorn Sorghum, *S. vulgare* var. *technicum,* is more or less unique because of the development at the top of the strong stem of a long, loose, much-branched flower cluster which is known as the "tassel," "head," or technically the *panicle,* with numerous long, slim, straight, fibrous branches. The panicles or heads are cut off a few inches below the basal branches before the flowers are quite mature and then dried. These heads are threshed carefully so that the slender, wiry branches are not badly broken, and then several of them are bound together by wire or cord tó make coarse carpet brooms and brushes. The finer *whisk* brooms are made from dwarf varieties of the same plant. Broomcorn has been grown in southern and south-eastern Europe for centuries. It was introduced into the United States about 1800 and it is now principally grown in Illinois, Oklahoma, Kansas, and Colorado. It is said that broom-corn culture was introduced to American agriculture by Benjamin Franklin from viable seed that he found in a broom that came from Europe.

Many different kinds of coarse cultivated grasses are called millet. The most of these are small-seeded species and varieties that are grown as cereals and for forage. Since ancient times, they have been associated, and more or less confused, with the true sorghums. The millets have probably been known in cultivation longer than the sorghums; they were included in Chinese religious rites as early as 2,700 B.C. Millets may be grown in poor, dry soils, and under higher tempera-tures than can sorghums.

Fig. 49. Pearl Millet, showing the dense head, two views of a spike-let, and the grain. This species has been in cultivation since pre-historic times for its grain *(from Hitchcock).*

There are four principal kinds of millet that make up the bulk of the crop as it is grown today. These are Foxtail, *Setaria italica,* Proso or Broomcorn Millet, *Panicum miliaceum,* Pearl Millet, *Pennisetum glaucum,* and Sauwa or Japanese Millet, *Echinochloa frumentacea.* It will be noted that these species represent four different genera of grasses, but they are all included in the same general tribe of grasses, namely, the *Paniceae,* or Panic Grasses. The true sorghums are more closely related to the Sugar Cane and Bluestem Grasses which are classified in the tribe *Andropogoneae*.

One or more of the many recognized varieties of Foxtail Millet are extensively grown for forage in the East Indies, Japan, China, and India, southeastern Europe, and Russia, North Africa, Canada, and the United States. These are grown for human food in the Old World, but in our country as forage crops. Proso Millet is nearly always grown as a grain crop for mankind and livestock. Southern Russia is the center of production of this latter millet, some 80 million bushels of it being grown there annually. This variety is important also in the northern Great Plains region. Pearl Millet furnishes important food for the lower classes of people in India, Egypt, and Africa. This is a moisture-loving crop and it is grown in India during the wet period of the monsoonal year. Japanese Millet is produced to a limited extent as a forage plant, under which conditions it may produce several crops during the year. Its grain is widely used for human food in the Orient. A vigorous program of breeding and improvement of millets and sorghums has been going on as much as with the better-known cereals, in the last years.

There are several other species of millet which are of some value in certain localities, but they are not widely known or grown. Among these we may mention Texas Millet, *Panicum texanum*. This annual grass is a native of Texas and northern Mexico. It produces good hay on the bottom lands along rivers. It now appears that Sudan Grass is of much greater value in general as a cultivated pasture and forage crop in North America than any of the millets.

Yet, the sorghums and millets contribute many important values to mankind. Their scores of versatile varieties supply man with a surprising list of products. Feed for livestock, both grain and forage, hay, silage, and staple foods for man such as flour and syrup, and brooms for his floor and clothing constitute the leading values that we derive from these Old World grasses. They also furnish a wide variety of secondary items such as alcoholic beverages, fuel, mats, baskets, paper, construction materials, fences, and toys.

The sorghums and millets should become of increasing value to the western world as our agricultural pursuits become more and more intensified. They offer many important secondary values that will become of growing significance to us as we continue to improve the finer features of American agriculture, especially under the semiarid and arid conditions of the great natural grassland regions of the west.

CHAPTER 10

Sugar Cane

ALL LIFE IS BUILT UPON A FOUNDATION OF SUGAR. SUGAR CANE IS QUITE unique as compared with the other grasses that have been considered in this series of studies. This outstanding plant differs from the other economic grasses in the fact that it produces large quantities of cane sugar which are readily extracted from its sap and refined in perfectly stupendous volumes for direct use as human food. The grain of the cereals and the leafage of the forage grasses, although not composed of sugar, are nevertheless produced by the respective plants from the sugar and other foods that they manufacture. Those products, in turn, enter the food cycle of all living things. Pure white sugar yields about 1,857 calories of energy per pound, which is considerably higher than the energy values that we secure from meat and fish. The astounding significance of sugar cane is realized when we learn that an acre of that grass, under favorable conditions, will produce forty times the average food yield of corn or beans.

Man has always had a "sweet tooth." We may assume that primitive man long before the dawn of civilization discovered the delight and the value of sugar as it occurs in the fruits, stems, and roots of certain wild plants, and in the nests of wild bees. Honey, it may be noted, was a popular sweet and sweetening agent for many centuries before commercial sugar was available.

Modern plant science has established the fact that all green plants manufacture sugar. This process, known as *photosynthesis,* is the most significant feature of the regular daily work that such plants do since sugar is the essential foundation of all life. Most green plants use practically all of the sugar that they produce each day for the immediate demands of the time, as they continue to grow, form their new leaves, shoots, roots, flowers, fruits, and seeds. The direct need and constant utilization of this newly made sugar is so nearly complete

121

in most plants that little sugar tends to accumulate in the tissues. Plant physiology teaches us, too, that certain species of plants are favored with a mechanism for the manufacture of sugar so efficient that the plant finds itself in possession of a supply of sugar that is far beyond its immediate needs. This excess supply of sugar tends to accumulate in the tissues, or as is often said, it is "stored" in the various organs of the plant. Many other species tend to transform large quantities of sugar into starch, which is then stored away in the tissues of the seeds, stems, and roots. This starch may be changed into sugar once more and used at a later period in the activity and development of the plant (Fig. 50).

FIG. 50. The sugar cane plant showing the stems, leaves, the large bushy inflorescence, a small portion of the latter, and cluster of hairy spikelets *(from Hitchcock)*.

It was a great day for mankind when primitive man discovered these abundant reserves of sugars and starches in various plants. It also constitutes a notable period in the march of man when he learned to domesticate, cultivate, and care for those plants in such a way that they responded by "storing up" more and more of those valuable foods.

Those natural advances and favorable reactions came with exceeding slowness, for it is within comparatively recent centuries that refined sugar from such sources has come to be of abundant, wide, and general use throughout the world. When modern man, with his superior wisdom and productive capacity, really caught the vision of the global economic significance of this benefaction of green plants, he flung himself into the picture with vigor and success. Now we find that governments and empires, races and creeds, sickness and health, prosperity and panic, literally rise and fall in response to man's influence and control over sugar. But this is not the place in which to turn attention to monopolies, tariffs and cartels, to rates and subsidies, quantities and quotas, to sugar wars and political buncombe or other economic and social machinations that have marched with the history of sugar since it first became of international importance to this superior age of man.

Of the many plants that are known to produce a surplus of sugar in considerable quantity above their own immediate needs there are two species that today furnish practically the entire world supply of raw and refined sugar. These are very different kinds of plants, the Sugar Cane, which is a true grass, *Gramineae,* and the Sugar Beet, which is not a grass at all, but is characteristic of a very different group, *Chenopodiaceae,* of flowering plants which includes the common spinach. Sugar cane and sugar beet reveal a long list of extremely different biological and geographical features. They agree, however, in the concentration of such large quantities of sugar in their juices that they are the only competitors in the production of raw and refined sugar for modern civilization. Our study here will be confined to the sugar cane, since it is the grassy member of this unique and outstanding pair of vegetable benefactors.

The sugar cane does not grow wild in any part of the modern world. It is widely cultivated in tropical lands and in certain subtropical areas (Fig. 51). This unique plant that we grow today probably originated from some extinct, wild, saccharine grass of India or somewhere in tropical, southeastern Asia where it has been cultivated from great antiquity. The juice of sugar cane when it is changed to a crude form of unrefined brown sugar is known as *gur* in India today. This product is used in large quantities there because of its relatively low cost. The English word sugar is but a slight modification of the Hindu word *su-gur.*

Sugar cane spread westward from India or southeastern Asia in the early part of our era. It was grown in lower Mesopotamia about 600 A.D. The Arabs aided in introducing the plant into Egypt from where it was carried to Sicily and Spain a century later. Venetian merchant princes supplied the newly popularized sugar to the Europeans during the fourteenth and fifteenth centuries. Energetic Portuguese and Spanish travelers had taken sugar cane throughout the Mediterranean area, to the Canary Islands, Azores, and Cape Verde Islands and to West Africa before the journey of Columbus to America. The great Spanish navigator carried the plant to the West Indies where it became established by about 1506 A.D.

A sugar mill was built in Santo Domingo in 1515. That date properly marks the foundation of the sugar industry of the Caribbean region where, especially to Cuba, it has become of the utmost importance. The cultivation of sugar cane spread through the West Indies, Central America, South America, and Mexico during the following century. The Jesuits carried sugar cane from Santo Domingo to Louisiana in 1741. The production of sugar in Louisiana did not amount to much, however, until about fifty years later (1792), when it was recovered from sugar cane and grown upon land now included in the city of New Orleans. From this uncertain initial period, the production of sugar cane has expanded until that state now produces annually about 400,000 tons of refined sugar and 30,000,000 gallons of molasses.

Sugar cane is now widely grown in the warm, humid regions of the world (Fig. 51). Producing areas are distributed in fact from as far south as nearly 40° latitude in southeastern Australian, to about 30° North latitude in China, India, and the United States. Large quantities of cane are grown in the alluvial lands of the great Gangetic plain in India. The areas of greatest production lie, however, well within the belt bounded by the tropics. There are no clearly centralized belts of cane culture, unless one wishes to recognize as two such areas the vast region including India and the Southwest Pacific with Java, Hawaii, and the West Indies. The sugar crop of the world now totals 35,000,000 tons, of which about 22,000,000 are secured from sugar cane.

India usually heads the list of cane sugar producers with about 5 million tons annually (6,560,000 tons in 1943), and somewhat more than 25 per cent of the world total of between 20 and 22 million tons for a recent five-year period. It should be noted, however, that the enormous tonnage credited to India is somewhat misleading as compared with the output of other nations because India produces and uses much of its sugar in the form of "gur" which is unpurified or unrefined sugar. Many of the people of India prefer this relatively poor grade of sugar on account of religious dictates, and it is, of course, much cheaper than the refined product.

Cuba is usually second to India in the total bulk of production, but Cuba's sugar is of the highly refined grade. Sugar is the most important product of Cuba upon which depends the prosperity of the island. Cuba leads the world not only in the production, but also in the exportation, of refined cane sugar. That West Indian island has yielded as much as 5.2 million tons of sugar and an enormous gallonage of molasses in one year as in the seasons of 1924–1925 and

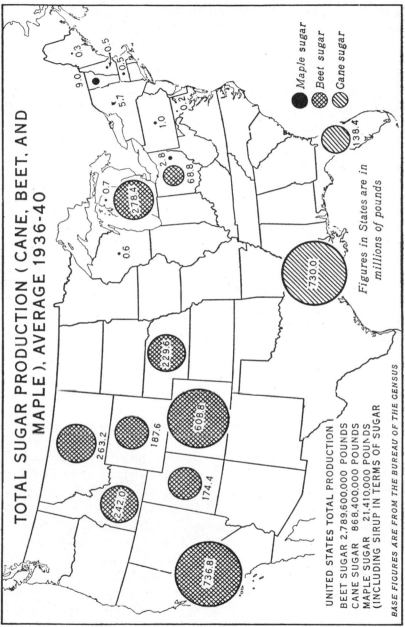

Maple sugar

Beet sugar

Cane sugar

Figures in States are in millions of pounds

0.3

0.5

0.5

0.5

9.0

5.7

1.0

0.2

138.4

2.8

68.8

278.4

0.7

0.6

730.0

229.6

263.2

187.6

608.8

174.4

242.0

736.8

UNITED STATES TOTAL PRODUCTION
BEET SUGAR 2,789,600,000 POUNDS
CANE SUGAR 868,400,000 POUNDS
MAPLE SUGAR 21,410,000 POUNDS
(INCLUDING SIRUP IN TERMS OF SUGAR

BASE FIGURES ARE FROM THE BUREAU OF THE CENSUS

Fig. 52. Total average production of sugar in the United States for the period 1936–1940, including sugar from sugarcane, beets, and maple trees. *(Photo from Bureau of Agricultural Economics, U. S. Department of Agriculture.)*

1928–1929.   Even for the five-year period beginning with 1925 she produced an average of 4.7 million tons per year.   Since 1941 production has ranged from 3,800,000 tons to 4,738,000 tons.   The ready market for Cuban sugar in the United States, together with certain international trade agreements and American capital that favor the industry, have been significant features in the rapid development of the sugar business in Cuba during the past thirty years.   During the boom years immediately preceding the first World War, 92 per cent of her exports of raw sugar came to the United States.

Other important sugar producers in the Caribbean area are Puerto Rico, the Dominican Republic, and the British West Indies.   The cultivation of sugar cane could probably be still further expanded in that region.   Puerto Rico produces about 1,000,000 tons per year.

Enormous quantities of sugar are produced in Java and the Philippine Islands.   Java commonly leads that area with about 2.0 million tons, while the Philippines produce about 1.2 million tons annually. Java exports a very large proportion of her sugar to India and the Far East.   The sugar crops of both Java and Cuba are favored by what are perhaps the world's finest combinations of savanna climate and soils for sugar cane agriculture of the intensive plantation type.

The desperate need for sugar in Japan in recent years has been reflected by the intensification of sugar culture in Formosa (Taiwan) which she took from China in 1895.   That mountainous island of less than 14,000 square miles and a population of more than five million has undergone a system of intense colonization and control under the Japanese.   This has resulted in the expansion and great improvement of sugar production in the savanna climate of West Formosa, as well as in the conservation of her export trade in other products, such as camphor and tea.   Formosa now probably produces more than one million tons of sugar annually.

Considerable sugar is produced in South America.   Brazil leads the continent with from 1,000,000 to 1,400,000 tons yearly, but the industry is on a very uncertain basis.   It would seem that the natural potentialities for sugar production in Brazil are practically limitless. Argentina produces about 400,000 tons, largely in the province of Tucuman.   Peru produces about 450,000 tons of sugar.   Much of this is grown on the large estates or sugar *haciendas* in the irrigated valleys, mostly north of Lima.   Some cane is also grown in Venezuela and Colombia, but the sugar produced there is mostly of local importance only.   Various economic, industrial, and social problems, together with difficulties in the matter of transportation have seriously bothered the development of the sugar industry of South America, despite the favorable natural conditions that should support very heavy sugar production, particularly in Brazil.

The Union of South Africa produces around 500,000 tons of sugar per year. The cultivation of sugar cane in Australia, especially centering in Queensland, is favored by protective laws in what would otherwise be an unprofitable and unfavorable situation. The output of cane sugar in Australia is about 700,000 tons annually.

The need of irrigation and soil fertilization tend to limit the output of sugar in the oceanic climate of Hawaii. But in spite of these difficulties the islands normally produce from 900,000 to 1,000,000 tons annually, a large proportion of which is exported.

In the continental United States sugar cane is extensively grown for sugar only in southern Louisiana, southeastern Texas, and in the Everglades of Florida. The industry has been developed in Louisiana from the original introduction of the crop about one hundred fifty years ago. Some 245,000 acres are now devoted to the crop in that state, and annual yields of 500,000 tons or more are not uncommon. The areas and yields in Texas and Florida are much lower, but the Florida field appears to be of increasing importance. Florida produced 99,000 tons of cane sugar and 6,000,000 gallons blackstrap molasses in 1945. On the whole the United States is making an important and noteworthy contribution to the world's supply of sugar, in spite of the relatively small area within which the successful cultivation of sugar cane is now limited. Mexico now produces about 400,000 tons of sugar per year.

Sugar cane is also grown in the southern United States for the production of cane syrup. The crop is managed for this purpose in eastern Texas, thence eastward through Louisiana, the southern half of Mississippi, Alabama, Georgia, and South Carolina.

Sugar cane is one of the globe's most distinctly tropical major economic plants. The profitable cultivation of sugar cane is practically restricted to a frost-free climate. The most of the varieties of sugar cane require a long growing season of as much as twelve or more months. The plant requires continuously high temperatures of 70° F. or preferably of 80° to 85° F. and this condition is met only in the belt of continuously warm climates. Cane also demands ample sunshine and much moisture as well as moderate temperature during the major period of its growth. The typical atmosphere of the humid tropics encourages the growth of the tall thick canes that are rich in sugar. Dry, sunny and less humid weather is especially important during the ripening period of the crop since that type of weather greatly favors the accumulation of the maximum quantity of sugar in the juice. Sugar cane does not do well in the permanently wet tropics with low sunshine, as for instance in the Amazon basin or in the Congo region of Africa. The ideal climate for sugar cane combines an abundance of precipitation, say 50 to 60 inches or more, continuous temperatures of 75° to 85° F., and an abundance of sunshine especially during a short, less humid ripening season. These climatic conditions determine the location of the most important commercial plantations of sugar cane, and the maximum yields of sugar in such areas.

Sugar cane cultivation also occurs to some extent outside the humid tropical regions as in the subtropical portions of Louisiana and Argentina, in India, and southern China. These are important areas, but the yield of sugar in such districts may be reduced by low temperature and drought. Irrigation aids in the production of heavy crops of sugar in Java, India, Formosa, Egypt, Puerto Rico, and Hawaii. Tropical windstorms of great fury sometimes damage the crop in the West Indies and in the Far East. The crop requires a growing season of from 20 to 24 months in the oceanic climate of the Hawaiian Islands. Expensive developments for irrigation, fertilization, and transportation have been necessary to insure a crop of cane on the leeward side (southwest) of the mountains in the islands. The crop of sugar cane in Peru is also dependent upon irrigation water.

Cuba and Java are the world's outstanding producers of cane sugar for export. If it were not for the occasional severe droughts the climate of Cuba would be ideal for sugar cane. The crop matures there in 12 to 15 months and several crops are secured from a given plantation without replanting each year. Cuban soils are good, and there is plenty of cheap land available. Although the cost of labor is relatively high, the natural conditions there favor expansion of the industry, especially toward the east and in the interior of the island. Tariff preference and American capital have greatly aided Cuba in the development of her sugar industry.

The volcanic soils of Java are very fertile, but the high price of land and the necessity of planting the crop each season are severe handicaps. The Dutch government has nevertheless developed a very efficient management of the industry that utilizes the abundant cheap labor of the island. The dry period of the monsoon insures a rich concentration of juice in the plants, and so Java produces the world's highest yields of sugar per acre.

An abundance of soil moisture, a ready supply of available nitrogen and other mineral nutrients, and a deep subsoil that favors the development of the root system are the principal features of good soils for the most profitable sugar cane farming. Heavy production is easily secured by the addition of supplemental fertilizers. Higher yields of sugar are secured if soil moisture is relatively low during the ripening season. This condition is, of course, easily managed under a system of irrigation.

Sugar cane and sugar beets differ widely in their climatic requirements, the latter being confined to the drier, temperate or intermediate types of climate of the middle latitudes. These two important crops are often cited as a fine example of the direct competition for world trade that involves an important basic product of the agriculture of very different climatic conditions and regions and supplied by quite different plants. However, true as this is, the complexities of international commerce have become so highly specialized and intensified during the past two decades, features especially critical during World War II, that numerous other examples of this sort of relationship are now of importance.

It should be clearly understood that *Sorghum,* often called sugar cane, is in reality not a *true* sugar cane in the strict botanical sense although it does produce considerable cane sugar. A species of sorghum, commonly known as "Guinea Corn," *S. saccharatum,* has been grown in China primarily for sugar, but is not the true sugar cane plant. Cultivated sugar cane as now grown commercially, throughout its commercial range, includes many varieties of several species of the genus *Saccharum.* These are mostly varieties of one species, namely *S. officinarum.* Varieties of *S. officinarum* are commonly known as *noble* canes. Two wild species of sugar cane are known to occur in southern Asia and the southwest Pacific. These are *S. robustum,* of New Guinea and Celebes, and *S. spontaneum,* which is distributed from Melanesia and Taiwan to Afghanistan. Both of these and other species, such as *S. barberi,* and *S. sinense,* have been used for breeding purposes by the modern breeders of sugar cane. Scores of varieties of sugar cane have been developed by these breeders over a period of many years of vigorous activity.

This plant is grown most extensively for the cane sugar which it produces. This food is one of our very finest biological fuels or sources of body energy which makes it a most valuable contribution to mankind. There are numerous other relationships and values that we associate with this wonder plant of the Orient. The sweetening effect that it imparts to food, even in small quantities, is a very important item in that more or less intangible principle that we call palatibility. Sugar makes *other* foods *good* or *better*.

The pure, white, granulated sugar of our modern dining tables is a beautiful material, practically pure chemically, and highly efficient as a supplier of energy to our tissues. The late E. E. Slosson once wrote: "Common sugar is an almost ideal food, cheap, clean, white, portable, imperishable, unadulterable, germ free, highly nutritious, completely soluble, altogether digestible, requires no cooking and leaves no residue. Its only fault is its perfection. It is so pure that man can not live on it." This product and its culture have been perfected after many centuries of study and improvement. The fine art and science of sugar refining and processing were not fully perfected until the nineteenth century. Syrup and molasses are also valuable as foods for man and beast because of their high sugar content. Sugar cane is widely grown in the south outside of Louisiana for syrup rather than for the sugar.

Alcoholic beverages of great variety are produced directly or indirectly by the fermentation of sugar. Rum and industrial alcohol are made from sugar molasses, a common product of sugar refining. The mass of crushed and ground fibrous stems of sugar cane that come from the sugar mills is known as *bagasse*. Bagasse is also utilized in the manufacture of insulating materials, wall board (of well-known brands), packing material, and even for low-grade paper and for certain purposes in the plastics industry. The refuse from the purification processes involved in sugar refining can be used as commercial fertilizer.

In addition to its old-time and ancient use in alcoholic fermentation, sugar has become one of the world's most important industrial chemicals in rather recent years. Already about 10,000 different sugar derivatives have been described by industrial chemists and chemical engineers. These are secured by fermentation and distillation and by other direct or indirect chemical transformations of sugar. The plastics industry is one of the most important fields for these newer uses. The total production of all types of plastics in the United States is now more than 500,000,000 pounds, and the output is growing rapidly each year. Many of these include sugar in the process of manufacture.

CHAPTER 11

Grasses of the Range, Pasture, and Meadow

ONE OF THE OLDEST AND MOST PRIMITIVE FEATURES OF HUMAN SOCIETY as it developed in association with the natural grasslands of the world was the simple practice of the nomads who wandered in the wake of their grazing flocks. That wearisome and ageless mark of man's earliest efforts to utilize the forage of the spacious grasslands and waste places of the earth was colorful, too, and full of adventure. Early pastoral life was hard and perilous. Civilization in general seems to have steadily moved forward by the slow but sure elimination of the most of the elements of hardship and danger that have faced society in its march along the grassland trailways of the globe.

These earliest phases of primitive agriculture were especially prominent in the broad arid grasslands and desert borders of Asia and Africa. Such rigorous, uncertain types of existence are still seen among certain of the peoples of those lands. The cowboy, the gaucho, the vaquero, the sheepherder, and the goatherd on the semiarid prairies and steppes of the Old World and the New, are today the more or less colorful and modern counterparts of the hardy types that characterized such lands before the first features of history were recorded. The motorized bunkhouse of a latter-day shepherd seen on the western range of the United States a few years ago seemed like a rude and shocking intrusion into an early type of environment that has changed but little, fundamentally, since the earliest times of the nomads.

Since the Middle Ages mankind has marched far toward a more varied and complete effort to reap the bountiful values that lie within the natural grasslands of the globe. The nomads and the herders were followed in many areas by the plowman and the cereals. The deep, rich soils of the savannas, steppes, and prairies began to yield their

131

bounty. Much error and failure dogged those primitive efforts for many years. But eventually an enormous expansion of the world's farmlands was more or less perfected. The glorious end of such fruit-ful efforts is not yet in view. True enough, the steppes, the pampas, and the prairies have long since become the bread baskets of the globe over which jealous leaders fight. That has been a notable achievement, but much more is yet to be done. Thrilling as this picture really is, man must still pause in awe before the great climatic and soils com-plex, that two-fold ruling barrier rigorously maintained by nature, which definitely limits his efforts to carry the varied trappings of modern civilization and diversified agriculture farther into the grass-lands. Tracts of prairie still retain a fair semblance of their old-time aspects. These virginal inheritances still seem best utilized by mod-ern man when he follows, in more or less modern manner, the practices of the pastoral ages. The natural cover of many broad areas of grassy lands may still best be made to yield their principal values to man by way of herds of cattle, bands of sheep, and flocks of goats, as of old.

THE OPEN RANGE

There remain immense expanses of more or less natural savanna, prairie, or steppe within all of the major grassland regions of the world. And this in spite of the fact that millions of acres of the original grasslands have been broken or ploughed and planted to cul-tivated crops, as has been noted in preceding chapters. Much of the unimproved land in western North America, for instance, is more or less open and even unfenced at this late date. This is what we call *the range* in our country. The *range* is an extensive, open, sparsely populated or unpopulated region of uncultivated natural grassland over which livestock may roam and feed more or less at will.

The climate of the range, in the meaning of the term used here—whether in the United States, Argentina, Africa, Australia, or Asia—is semiarid, or arid, and the vegetation, mostly grasses, is drought-resistant or drought-escaping. There are numerous characteristic spe-cies of legumes like clovers, vetches, and others, composites like asters, daisies and similar plants, and other natural groups of plants that are regularly found in association with the dominant grasses of the range. These broad acreages of grassland are also marked by a varied and dependent fauna that is quite as distinctive as the grasses, and very important as serving to complete the characteristic wild-life picture of the natural prairie as a whole.

The slow and toilsome march of mankind to enter the grasslands of the globe and the ultimate appropriation of their tremendous values may be recorded as a series of major phases or epochs. That story had its real beginning at the early time in the long geological calendar when nature was perfecting the main features of the climate, soils, and natural vegetation of the prairies. Those early prairies were peopled with herds of wild, grazing animals, merely the last vestiges of whose modern representatives are still with us. Man marched into this environment at a much later period and he sought his food and raiment from the indigenous animals and plants that were about him. Somewhat later he was more or less successful in semi-domesticating certain wild animals, and he himself became semi-civilized. Much later he became so resourceful that he began to break the soil and to cultivate certain plants, notably the grasses. Only yesterday, as earth's total history imperfectly reveals itself, has man become a diversified agriculturist and an industrial giant. He is still far from the completion of the global social pattern that will contribute the final chapter or epoch of the thrilling epic. We can never escape the fundamental control exercised by the foods which stem originally from the grasslands.

The nomads of Saudi Arabia and the Takla Makan still trail their flocks as of old. Our American ranchmen load their motor trucks with choice Shorthorn and Hereford beeves and deliver them to the market at top prices. This contrast spans six millenia or more of mankind's history since he first approached the essential problems posed by the grasslands of the globe.

The boundless extent of the North American prairies was first revealed to the white man by the daring explorer, Coronado. That hardy Spaniard marched northeastward from Mexico in 1540, with the principal objective of locating the fabled *Seven Cities of Cibola* whose streets were said to be paved with gold. His expedition went far into the grasslands and finally crossed the prairies to what is now Kansas and southern Nebraska. Coronado did not find cities paved with gold, but he did leave some vivid records of the nature of the grassland over which his ill-fated expedition plodded its weary way.

Later explorations, especially from the east, revealed that the American prairies supported enormous numbers of wild, grazing mammals that roamed hither and yon over the rich, virgin grassland. Millions of bison, elk, deer, and antelope seemed to reveal the possibilities of the spacious natural ranges for livestock production. But it was nearly four hundred years after Coronado's famous march that

American stockmen began a vigorous assault upon the forage resources of the prairies.

Strenuous, picturesque, and successful efforts to utilize these natural resources began in the United States about the middle of the past century. The extension of the railroads across the prairies and the subjugation of the Red Man enabled the White Man to enter that great natural domain with comparative ease, to establish homes, and to remain in safety. He could then market his produce advantageously. The importance to the nation of the development of these natural resources cannot be over-estimated. Statistics from a recent year indicate that the range lands of the western states produced about 33 per cent of all of the cattle and calves marketed in the United States. And in addition, the same states produced about 55 per cent of the total lamb and sheep crop of the country and 75 per cent of the wool and mohair. These events and many other significant developments within our prairie lands that are constantly yielding enormous values to the nation and the world, have taken place within the memory of men, the last of whom are only now passing from the stirring scenes of the grassland frontier. The complete story of our prairie range with its colorful details is one of the most dynamic and distinctive features of American history, as indeed it is of the grasslands of the world as a whole.

Extensive natural ranges that are of tremendous value because of the livestock that they directly support are found within all of the world's major grassland regions (Fig. 6). The most extensive of these are in Africa, Soviet Russia, South America, Australia, and North America (Fig. 6). Hundreds of millions of acres of native savanna, prairie, and steppe in these countries produce livestock in such volume as to supply a major element to the commerce of the world. The range lands of the western United States including both forested and unforested areas embrace the enormous acreage of more than 700,000,000 acres which lie mostly west of the one-hundredth meridian. The numerous industries whose very existence depends upon this relationship are noteworthy elements of modern society. Smaller areas in this and other lands and on the borders of the world's great deserts also transport a goodly share of the natural values of the native wild grasses and other forage plants to the welfare of mankind across a bridge of domesticated herds. The conditions of life, and even the important native grasses concerned, are much the same in the widely separated regions across the globe.

The principal general features of the climatic conditions and the soils that are characteristically associated with the wild and domesticated life of the unforested range have been mentioned in our earlier treatment of the major grasslands of the world. Man cannot change or control the climate of the range to suit himself. Neither can he change the fundamental nature and value of the soils of the range except by tillage, cropping, irrigation, and the application of fertilizers. These principles of soil management can be best applied with profit on only a small proportion of the range, because of the limited supply of water and the relentless and oftentimes ruthless domination of the climatic controls that prevail.

The open range is utilized to its best degree, as long as the present climate prevails, if it is managed in such a manner as to enable livestock to reap its finest natural returns directly from the grasses that nature has perfected for just such purposes. It is indeed fortunate that those now in charge of the practical and scientific management of our great natural grassland areas in the western United States understand that vast expanses of such lands must be preserved forever as ranges. Since these intricate problems involve one of the world's major industries as it may be handled in our American grassland "empire" of about 700,000,000 acres, they are, indeed, matters of fundamental national concern to every American.

NOTABLE RANGE GRASSES OF THE UNITED STATES

The range area of western United States is one of the richest natural grasslands of the world in the variety and number of species of its native grasses. The largest type of range, the short-grass type, is spread over about 198,000,000 acres which lies mostly on the high plains. The more important and prominent grasses that are found here are the Blue Grama, *Bouteloua gracilis*, Buffalo Grass, *Buchloë dactyloides*, Bluestem Wheatgrass, *Agropyron smithii*, and Curly Mesquite, *Hilaria belangeri*. To the east of the short-grass type lies the tall-grass range, covering about 18,000,000 acres. The latter region is the characteristic home of the Slender Wheatgrass, *Agropyron pauciflorum*, the Big and Little Bluestem Grasses, *Andropogon furcatus*, *A. scoparius*, and the Porcupine Grass, *Stipa spartea*. Other large range areas are found in the sagebrush lands over the northern half of the Great Basin country between the Rockies and the Cascades. Scattered among the sagebrush plants there one finds the Bluebunch Wheatgrass,

Agropyron spicatum, Indian Ricegrass, *Oryzopsis hymenoides,* and several species of the Porcupine or Needle Grasses, *Stipa* spp. The sagebrush type of range covers about 96,000,000 acres. Sometimes a fourth major range area is designated as the Pacific Type, with about 42,000,000 acres which lies mostly in Washington, Oregon, and California. Prominent grasses there are Bluebunch Wheatgrass, Sandberg's Bluegrass, Giant Wild Rye, and California Needlegrass. Other prominent species of grasses are of local value and still others are worthless and troublesome weeds in all of these types. Many of them, however, are of wide distribution and of major value for forage. We have selected but a few of the most valuable and better-known or more noteworthy species of the American range for listing and brief discussion in this place.

Buffalo Grass, *Buchloë dactyloides,* is one of the most famous of all native American grasses (Fig. 10). This grass grows naturally nowhere else in the world. Its principal area of distribution is from central Texas northward to North Dakota and southeastern Montana, and thence southward across eastern Wyoming and Colorado, Arizona and New Mexico. The species is often seen to the east and west as well as north and south of this main area, but it is of minor importance in such marginal areas. This area includes a large part of the semiarid region of the United States that is commonly known as the "short-grass plains" and the "dry plains." It comprises a large part of the vast terrain over which the Bison or American Buffalo grazed in the early days.

Buffalo Grass is a hardy perennial and it grows in characteristic low, close, gray-green colonies a few feet in diameter, or more often in the form of continuous pure stands of turf consisting of tough roots and short stems a few inches tall bearing curly leaves. It spreads extensively by means of slender surface runners (Fig. 10). Being notoriously nutritious both in fresh and dry state, it is nearly an ideal species for all-year forage for wild animals and livestock.

The thick, tenacious sod of Buffalo Grass was cut into blocks and used by the early settlers of the region to build the walls of their sod houses. Such houses, when well roofed and plastered, provided comfortable homes for the ranchers and settlers for many years. This grass is also of great value in soil conservation.

Blue Grama, *Bouteloua gracilis,* is another famous, densely tufted perennial American grass (Fig. 11). It is a common companion and close relative of Buffalo Grass. This grass is found not only throughout the range of Buffalo Grass but it occurs more widely in Arizona, Colorado, Wyoming, Montana, Utah, southern Nevada, and southeastern California, as well as in Nebraska, Missouri, Illinois, and Wisconsin, and northward into Manitoba and Alberta. The broad, north and south belt of greatest importance of these two premier American grasses lies westward from the meridian of central Kansas and Nebraska, to the eastern foothills of the Rocky Mountains, and from northern Mexico well into Canada. This is an area of about 280,000,-000, acres, about two-thirds of which is now more or less well managed as range land. Blue Grama usually forms a low, close, continuous cover, much like that formed by Buffalo Grass, that extends over vast expanses of the dry plains. Blue Grama and Buffalo Grass are often closely associated in the same cover and over hundreds of square miles of the semiarid central plains.

Grama Grass has certain habits of growth (lacking the runners) and certain structural features that closely resemble Buffalo Grass. The two species are often confused by those with little training in the taxonomy of the grasses. They have been highly prized by livestock men ever since they were discovered.

Side-oats Grama, *Bouteloua curtipendula* (Fig. 53), is a close relative of the Blue Grama and is found not only throughout the range of the latter, but it is widely distributed eastward across the true prairies to Ontario and Maine, and southward to Maryland, Tennessee, and Alabama. This is a taller and more luxuriant grass than Blue Grama and it is quite at home in the deep, dark soils of the tall-grass prairies of the more humid middle-western grasslands. It is very nutritious too, and it is highly valued as a meadow grass and wild hay plant.

Black Grama, *Bouteloua eriopoda,* is another species of this important American genus that is found only in the southwestern states of Utah, Arizona, New Mexico, western Texas, and in northern Mexico. It is common on the dry hills and mesas of that picturesque region across which Coronado and his men marched on the disappointing journey of 1540. The stands of grass are rather thin in the more arid portions of that region, but whenever Black Grama is found it stamps the place with real forage value because of its vigor and its high palatability and nutritiousness when fresh or dry. Black Grama is a fine example of the real quality that is developed by a native plant under the extremely hazardous conditions of the desert.

Two very interesting associates of Black Grama and the desert environment of the same general region are the valuable and distinctive Curly Mesquite Grass (Fig. 13), *Hilaria belangeri,* and Tabosa Grass, *Hilaria mutica.* These are somewhat like the *Boutelouas,* but they are members of a different natural tribe of grasses. They are often very prominent features of the vegetation of the southwestern desert landscapes.

The Big Bluestem, *Andropogon furcatus,* is one of the most characteristic and conspicuous species of the eastern or tall-grass portion of the American prairies (Fig. 7). This area lies between the short-grass area with its Gramas and Buffalo Grass and the western edge or border of the eastern deciduous forest region of North America. The grass is found, however, far beyond the typical tall-grass prairie; in fact it occurs in the prairie provinces of western Canada and in all the range states except Idaho and Nevada. It also occurs in the states of the Pacific Coast, and it extends southward into Mexico as well.

The sod of the more humid portions of the rolling, tall-grass prairie of the Middle West, wherein this species was most dominant and is most at home, is now largely broken and planted to cultivated crops. The species is seldom found within that area except in sites that are unfavorable for crops or in isolated remnants of the original prairie which are pastured or cut for wild hay. It is often seen in open woods and clearings and along roadsides throughout the east. Big Bluestem is one of the most robust and colorful of all the numerous native species of the American prairies. Its erect, leafy tufts are sometimes as tall as ten feet or even taller in especially good sites, but as a rule they vary from three to six feet high. The long culms that bear at the top two or three slender widely divergent purple or yellowish clusters of spikelets, are among the most notable details of our prairie flora. This is a very fine species for forage and hay.

The Little Bluestem, *Andropogon scoparius,* is a close relative and associate of the Big Bluestem, being found over practically the same vast expanse of country as the latter (Fig. 8). The Little Bluestem, however, is more characteristic of *upland* prairies, whereas Big Bluestem prefers the *lowlands.* The dense tufts of rigid culms about two to three feet high are often seen in the lighter soils of upland prairies, where the species takes a significant role in the natural succession following overgrazing of the range. The stems and leaves of the bluestems turn to a bright reddish-brown color in the fall which produces a very striking glow over the prairie landscape in winter.

Close associates of the above bluestems are other genera and species of grasses in great numbers. Among the more prominent of these, we may mention *Stipa,* the Needle Grasses and Porcupine Grasses, especially *S. spartea,* mainly of the East, *S. comata,* of the West, and *S. leucotricha* of the South, Side-oats Grama, *Bouteloua curtipendula,* June Grass, *Koeleria cristata,* Indian Grass, *Sorghastrum nutans,* Switch Grass, *Panicum virgatum,* Dropseed Grass, *Sporobolus hetero-*

FIG. 53. Side-oats Grama, a unique grass of the North American prairie *(from Hitchcock).*

FIG. 54. June Grass, good for forage in the native pastures of the Western States *(from Hitchcock).*

lepis, Wheat Grasses, *Agropyron spicatum,* and *A. smithii.* The Wire Grasses, *Aristida purpurea,* and *A. longiseta,* and Galleta, *Hilaria jamesii* (Fig. 57) are also commonly seen in the short-grass, the tall-grass, or desert portions of our great American grasslands. The Sand Reed, *Calamovilfa longifolia* is often seen in sand soils in this region. Certain grasses of the range that are commonly regarded as worthless weeds may be of considerable forage value at certain times of the year or under certain conditions. Thus Downy Chess or Bronco Grass, *Bromus tectorum* (Fig. 56), is highly regarded by many stockmen for early season grazing on the arid ranges of Nevada.

There are vast ranges, especially for sheep, in extreme Southern Patagonia. Certain of the great ranches or *estancias* there cover as much as 300,000 acres and carry as many as 125,000 head of sheep. Tussock Grass, *Deschampsia caespitosa, D. antarctica,* and various species of Bluegrasses and Fescue Grasses, especially the native Sheep's Fescue, *F. magellanica,* are found over those ranches. Patagonian lamb and mutton are said to compare favorably with any from New Zealand, and these meats are popular in England. The meat is frozen for export trade in large modern freezing works known as *frigorificos.* One such freezing plant lies near Punta Arenas on the Straits of Magellan.

FIG. 55. Switchgrass, common in the eastern portions of the North American prairies and good for wild hay *(from Hitchcock).*

FIG. 56. Downy Chess, a widespread grass that is good in season, but better known as a nasty weed *(from Hitchcock).*

The peculiar climatic, biological, and economic features of those great open places that constitute our western range in the United States, demand that such lands be forever managed for livestock production. The region as a whole has been badly mismanaged and overgrazed in the past, but a wiser and more scientific approach to the problems involved now seem to promise better times for the future. But the old conflicts between diversified farming with its cultivated crops and the range livestock ranchman with their cattle and sheep problems will doubtless continue to delay the acceptance of nature's best program for the range. Weather cycles and international crises tend to focus the attention of the nation upon the bare necessities of food production on an enormous scale and these conditions have sometimes seriously modified what would be the most sensible attitudes toward the best uses of range lands.

FIG. 57. Galleta Grass, a unique grass of the American grasslands from Wyoming to Mexico and southern California *(from Hitchcock)*.

PASTURES AND PASTURE GRASSES

A *pasture* may be defined as a restricted and commonly fenced area of land that is dominated by grasses or other forage plants and used more or less naturally by grazing animals. Pastures may contain many other kinds of plants besides grasses. Much of the primitive forage value of certain wild pastures is supplied, in fact, by the leaves and twigs of shrubs and other woody plants known as *browse,* upon which animals feed. We are considering here relatively small areas, the grassy pastures, such as are commonly fenced and grazed by cattle, sheep, or horses. The *range* as we have considered it in the preceding sections may be thought of as a very extensive, natural, permanent grassland pasture, and commonly unfenced or fenced on a very broad scale. We will use the term *pasture* for a very much smaller area of grassland that is usually fenced. The pasture, in this sense, may be native, natural or *wild*, that is, composed of native grasses, or it may be a *tame* or improved pasture, that is, composed of domesticated, cultivated, or introduced grasses or other plants.

Pastures are either permanent or temporary. They may be small, fenced portions of the extensive natural range with its native grasses, and often close to the settlement or ranch home; or they may be relatively small fenced areas of the general farm land, far removed from the open range, upon which annual or perennial, native or introduced grasses are sown and maintained for direct grazing purposes. The following treatment utilizes the last characterization of pastures. This is essentially the pasture of a farm upon which most of the land is used for cultivated crops, as is common to the general farms of the tall-grass prairies and those of the corn belt, wheat belt, dairy belt, and cotton belt of the United States. One may recognize a real *dairy* belt or *pasture* belt in northeastern United States, especially to the north and east of the corn belt. There are extenisve pasture lands in other parts of the world, too, notably in Argentina, Australia, Africa, and on a smaller scale in Great Britain.

The original fenced pastures of our American grasslands were merely small enclosures of native vegetation close to the home and into which the settlers could turn their ponies, their horses and milk cows when they were not in the stables. The grasses of those pastures were the species that grew naturally in the immediately adjacent region. However, those native or wild pastures were soon depleted or worn out by overpasturage, or by heavy use plus severe damage by climatic conditions, such as drought, and by erosion. Such abused pastures often became invaded and completely taken over by worthless weeds. Then the farmer commonly plowed up the pasture and put it into the usual crops or tried to establish a new pasture by artificial seeding.

An interesting and important change that recently took place in many overgrazed native pastures of the less humid tall-grass prairie region—the corn belt—of the United States was the complete replacement of the native cover by Kentucky Bluegrass, *Poa pratensis,* a species that is native to Europe. Bluegrass is a fine species for the northern pasture, but it is not nearly as drought-resistant as are the native prairie grasses. Consequently, after many years of excellent pasturage, those fine Bluegrass pastures of the western portion of the corn belt become badly damaged or completely destroyed by the recurrence of periods of severe drought, such as that of 1934 to 1938. During such crises the farmers were severely harassed in their efforts to secure pasturage for even a few milk cows and horses. They sought help by sowing temporary pastures of wheat, oats, brome grass, or some other quickly growing plant. Under less arid conditions the maintenance of excellent permanent grassy pastures is easily accomplished, but even then such resources must be managed with considerable forethought including soil requirements if they are to retain their full capability.

Domesticated pasture grasses show a wide range in their preference for climatic and soil conditions as do the cereals and other crops. Of the numerous species of grasses that are used for improved pastures in the United States we find that those that have been introduced from foreign countries have taken high place. Some do best in cool, dry, or humid climates, others in humid subtropical climates, some in light, sandy soils, others in heavier soils. A few of the more successful and valuable pasture grasses may be indicated.

The Kentucky Bluegrass, *Poa pratensis,* which was introduced from Europe many years ago, has proved to be one of the very finest grasses for American pastures (Fig. 58). This grass is representative of some two hundred or more species of *Poa* that

Fig. 58. Kentucky Bluegrass, also called June Grass, is one of the best known grasses in the United States and is widely used for lawns and pastures *(from Hitchcock).*

are widely scattered over the globe, especially under the influence of the intermediate and cold climates. More than sixty species of *Poa* occur in the United States. The plant which we know as Kentucky Bluegrass is a perennial and was originally described by Linnaeus as *Poa pratensis* in his *Flora of Lapland,* which was published in 1737.

Its common American name merely reflects the fact that it has become a prominent feature of the agriculture of Kentucky. The Bluegrass region of that state is a notable pasture area in which this species is prominent, but the plant is not native to Kentucky.

Kentucky Bluegrass is especially valuable throughout the cool, humid, northern portions of the eastern United States and southeastern Canada, from North Carolina, Tennessee, and eastern Oklahoma northward. It is resistant to cold, but high temperatures, whether in humid or arid regions, are detrimental to it. Its westward limits are set by the increasing aridity and high summer temperatures of the climate of the plains. The bluegrass often escapes destruction in the more severe western portions by its ability to live through prolonged periods of late summer drought. During this more or less dormant phase it becomes exceedingly dry and may appear quite dead, but with the coming of more humid and cooler weather in the fall or early spring it becomes green and fresh once more. If the periods of summer heat are excessive and these follow periods of relative low precipitation during the fore-summer, and if this combination is repeated for a succession of years, then Bluegrass may succumb. This situation was widely prevalent in the tall-grass prairie region of the west during the great drought of the 1930's. This was a real crisis for the farmers of those areas because the Bluegrass pastures were often completely destroyed. But in the long run this species has proven to be one of the very best of all pasture grasses within the general region indicated. It is also excellent for irrigated pastures and lawns in a much more extensive area.

Fig. 59. Orchard Grass, fine for meadows and pastures in the more humid portions of the prairies *(from Hitchcock).*

A bluegrass seed industry has been developed in the United States during the past few years. The area of greatest seed production now includes North and South Dakota, Nebraska, Kansas, Missouri, Iowa, and Minnesota. One county in Nebraska produces $500,000 worth of bluegrass seed each year. The total production for Nebraska for 1947 has been estimated as 1,000,000 bushels.

Orchard Grass or Cocksfoot, *Dactylis glomerata,* is another species (Fig. 59) that is popular for our northern pastures. This excellent perennial was also introduced from Europe and is now widely naturalized in the United States, Canada, and Newfoundland, southeastern Alaska, and southward to Florida and California. It is an important grass in northern Idaho, and from western Washington to northern California. Orchard Grass is of greatest importance as a pasture plant throughout the corn belt, but it also does well in the northern stretches of the cotton belt. This excellent and luxurious grass furnishes abundant and nutritious pasturage especially in spring and early summer as well as in late autumn.

Tall Oat Grass, *Arrhenatherum elatius,* is a widely-known and grown pasture grass, especially in its native Europe. It was brought to the United States early in the nineteenth century, and it has since escaped from cultivation to become widely scattered from Newfoundland to British Columbia and southward over about the same territory as Orchard Grass, which it closely resembles in its climatic requirements. Within their climatic range in this country Tall Oat Grass does best as a pasture plant on light, sandy or gravelly soils, whereas Orchard Grass does best on heavier, loamy, moist soils. This species is perhaps of more importance in the long run as a hay grass than as a pasture grass, since it does not endure prolonged cropping and trampling by grazing animals.

Fig. 60. Bermuda Grass, a native of the Mediterranean region, has become a very valuable grass for pastures and lawns in the southern states *(from Hitchcock).*

Tall Oat Grass is of much importance in Europe where it is regarded as one of the best species for pastures, especially in France, Germany, and Switzerland.

Bermuda Grass, *Cynodon dactylon,* is to the southern and south-eastern United States about what Bluegrass is to the northern and northeastern section of our country, although, of course, the two species are sparingly but widely scattered through the common central border of their range (Fig. 60). This grass was brought to the United States from the tropical lands of the Old World where it is a native of India. Bermuda Grass is most at home in pastures and other open fields and waste places from Maryland to Florida and westward to eastern Oklahoma, Texas, southern New Mexico, Arizona, and California. It is one of the most valuable pasture and lawn grasses of the southern states. Bermuda Grass readily adjusts itself to a wide variety of soils, but it favors a moist, well-drained soil. It, like Kentucky Bluegrass, frequently invades other kinds of pastures and meadows and so may often become a *weed* in that sense. The value of Bermuda Grass is often cut short by lowering temperature in late summer, just as the vegetative season of Kentucky Bluegrass is terminated in the north by the dry weather of the after-summer.

Dallis Grass, *Paspalum dilatatum,* is another interesting grass of the warm, humid southland. This grass was introduced from the region of northern Argentina and Uruguay, its native home. It is now to be found from New Jersey to Florida, and westward to Tennessee, Oklahoma, and Texas, as well as in some of the far western states. The species prefers rich, black soils and moist bottomlands. Dallis Grass tends to grow in tufts and it produces an abundance of pasturage for most of the year in the more humid areas of the cotton belt. It is also grown in Australia (New South Wales), Scotland, and northern England where it produces an abundance of green feed.

Smooth Brome, *Bromus inermis,* is another notable pasture grass of Europe and Asia that has been introduced into North and South America and is widely grown with great success. The species (Fig. 61) is very widely distributed across Europe and Asia. In contrast to Kenutcky Bluegrass and Bermuda Grass, Smooth Brome is quite at home in dry climates. The species is sometimes called Hungarian Brome, and thus we have a reflection of its importance in Hungary where it is extensively grown as a pasture plant on the plains. It is widely adaptable and is now one of the most important cultivated grasses of the pastures in the central and northern Great Plains region of North America and the inter-mountain states. It is used over a vast region from northern

Arizona and Kansas, to Iowa, Minnesota, Utah, eastern Oregon and Washington, and into the prairie provinces of Canada. Smooth Brome is also a very important pasture grass in Argentina where it contributes (along with alfalfa) to the fattening of the famous herds of cattle on the pampa.

This grass is a tall, long-lived perennial that endures much natural hardship and produces an abundance of palatable pasturage. It also successfully endures the rigorous treatment administered by grazing animals. It does well even in rather dry, sandy soils, where its sodforming habit is of great value. In recent years Smooth Brome has been widely used in the reseeding of western ranges and for planting along highways in the west. So great has become the demand for seed of this grass that many farmers find that it is profitable to grow certified Brome Grass seed for the market. Many states are now growing this seed. Nebraska produced about 45 per cent of all Smooth Brome Grass seed in the United States in 1944.

The Wheat Grasses, that is, species of *Agropyron,* are representative of a genus which includes about sixty species of grasses that are widely distributed through the intermediate climates of both hemispheres. Western Wheat Grass, *A. smithii,* and Slender Wheat Grass, *A. pauciflorum,* are both natives of North America, while the Crested Wheat Grass, *A. cristatum,* is a drought-resistant native of the steppes of Soviet Russia. These three species are among the most valuable grasses known for pasture and hay production. Western

Fig. 61. Smooth Brome Grass, also called Hungarian Brome (from its native land), is widely cultivated in the northern Great Plains for pasture and hay *(from Hitchcock).*

Wheat Grass is quite at home in the dry northern plains, where it occurs in extensive pure stands especially on heavy soils, and in mixture with other native grasses. Slender Wheat Grass is often seen on rich soils along streams and in valleys as well as on dry tablelands and alkali flats. This species is now widely sown for pastures in the Dakotas and in the provinces of Canada, where it competes with Smooth Brome as a pasture plant. The Russian species, Crested Wheat Grass, is highly drought-resistant and it is now extensively grown in the dry northwestern states. It has been widely sown as a pasture grass, and it has been recently used also to reseed the overgrazed ranges in the northern Great Plains and intermountain states. Crested Wheat Grass does well where it is too dry for Smooth Brome or the other two species of Wheat Grasses. And so we have again, in this exotic species, rather recently introduced from a distant land, a very valuable pasture grass whose worth has already been demonstrated and whose further widespread values here seem to be assured.

The natural range and pasture lands of Australia are characterized by many interesting grasses that are not common in other grassland regions. Some of the more important of these species are the Mitchell Grasses, *Astrebla lappacea,* the Curley Mitchell Grass, and *A. elymoides,* the Hoop Mitchell Grass, *A. squarrosa,* the Bull Mitchell Grass, and *A. pectinata,* the Barley Mitchell Grass. The Australian Bluegrass, *Dichantheum sericeum,* and Lovegrass, *Eragrostis setifolia,* are also important in that region.

There are many other species of pasture grasses which would be considered in a more extensive and detailed treatment that would include much additional material from foreign lands. Many species might be included, for instance, in a treatment of the native and introduced pasture grasses of Argentina. Cogon Grass, *Imperata clyindrica,* is a tall grass of the warm climate grasslands of the Old World that is of value as a pasture plant. This is especially true of certain varieties of this species if they are grazed when the growth is rather young.

There are many other species of grasses, including several of the cereals, especially oats and rye, that are sown for supplemental or temporary pastures or for special types of pastures and in special places. Oats and rye are widely grown in Argentina for winter pastures.

MEADOWS AND MEADOW GRASSES

A grass *meadow* may be defined as a plot or field that is covered by leafy grasses and which is primarily managed for the *hay* that it produces. The grasses (or other plants) concerned are usually perennial species. The plots are often fenced in order to maintain the desired composition and density of the hay crop.

Hay is composed of a mixture of the dried stems and leaves of rather slender or fine-stemmed plants, commonly grasses, which are palatable and nutritious as a food for livestock. Alfalfa and various clovers are also widely grown for hay production. The total value of the hay crop in the United States, including all crops as well as grasses, is $760,000,000 annually. Hay is most commonly dried or *cured* by exposure of the cut plants to the wind and sun as they lie on the ground in the meadow. In very humid areas it is necessary to turn the cut plants frequently to hasten the curing process, or to spread the green hay on specially constructed perches, pyramids, or various types of frames or racks. Such practices remove the hay from the moist ground and facilitate the circulation of air through the curing hay. After the hay is fairly well cured it is either stacked in the meadow or farmyard or stored in sheds or barns from which it is readily fed. The details involved in the growth, preparation, storage, and feeding of hay under a great variety of climatic and economic conditions the world over are among the most varied and interesting features of the agriculture of the globe.

Numerous kinds of plants besides grasses are used for hay, but the true grasses are so varied and so widely and abundantly used for this purpose that most people, including many farmers, think of *hay* as always consisting of dry, or cured grasses. A moment's reflection, however, will serve to recall the fact that much hay is made from alfalfa and clover for instance, and that these plants are not grasses at all; in truth they are very distantly related to the grasses. We are concerned here only with hay that is made from the true grasses.

There is a rather well defined center of *wild* hay production, the Wild Hay Belt of the United States. This extends from northeastern Oklahoma across eastern Kansas, much of northern Nebraska, eastern Dakotas, and the southern half of Minnesota (Fig. 62). This is essentially a part of the Spring Wheat Belt also. Millions of tons of wild grass hay are cured every year within this area, much of which is shipped to the great metropolitan livestock markets. The total production of wild hay in the United States in 1944 was 141,000,000 tons. The wild hay cut in Nebraska for 1945 was 2,635,000 tons with a value of $18,972,000.

As we have noted in our treatment of the grassy pastures we find, too, that there are certain *wild* meadow grasses and certain *tame* or cultivated meadow grasses and that they may be of the same or different species. The wild hay grasses are nearly as widely scattered over

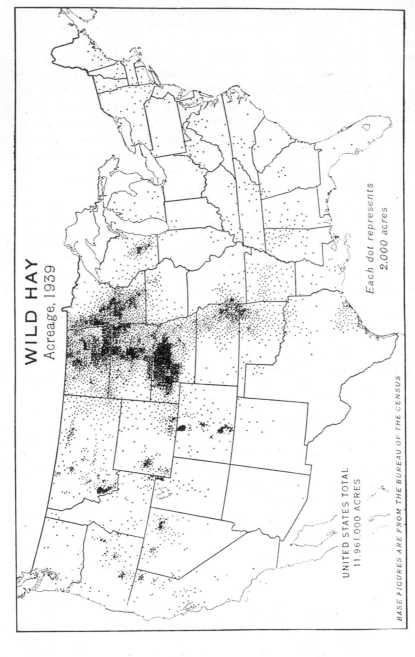

WILD HAY
Acreage, 1939

UNITED STATES TOTAL
11,961,000 ACRES

*Each dot represents
2,000 acres*

BASE FIGURES ARE FROM THE BUREAU OF THE CENSUS

Fig. 62. Location and acreages of wild hay in the United States for 1939. *(Photo from Bureau of Agricultural Economics, U. S. Department of Agriculture.)*

the globe as are the native grasslands themselves. There are many species of the native grasses of the globe that grow in a way that makes it readily possible and profitable to cut them and put them up as cured hay. To be profitable, such grasses must be palatable and nutritious and sufficiently luxuriant so as to yield such a quantity of good dried hay so that the extra work and expense involved in preparing it are justified. We may mention a few of the species of American grasses that are used for making wild prairie hay. Then we will consider some of the introduced grasses that are regularly used for tame hay.

Big Bluestem, *Andropogon furcatus,* and the Little Bluestem, *A. scoparius,* were cited as among the outstanding species of grasses in the tall-grass prairies of North America. The former is a lowland species, the latter an upland species, and they both enter into the composition of countless tons of the native prairie hay that is cut in Nebraska, Kansas, Oklahoma, and elsewhere. There are other species of much value too, such as Western Wheat Grass, *Agropyron smithii,* Needle Grass, *Stipa comata,* and *S. spartea* toward the western and northern portions of the region. Other tall-grass prairie species that enter into the hay crop in various areas are Indian Grass, *Sorghastrum nutans,* June Grass, *Koeleria cristata* (Fig. 54), Switch Grass, *Panicum virgatum* (Fig. 55), Prairie Cordgrass, or Sloughgrass, *Spartina pectinata,* and Silver Beardgrass, *Andropogon saccharoides.* These and still other species are of importance in the wild hap crop in the general region of the Spring Wheat Belt of the United States and elsewhere. Many other species yield wild hay of local importance in practically all of the states. Heavy stands of Bluejoint, *Calamagrostis canadensis,* and Reed Canary Grass, *Phalaris arundinacea,* furnish much hay from the low, more or less marshy meadows of the upper Mississippi valley region.

The cultivated meadow grasses of the United States are mostly species that have been introduced from foreign countries. Included among these are Timothy, Orchard Grass, the Bent Grasses, and Redtop.

Timothy, *Phleum pratense,* a native of Europe, northern Africa and northern Asia, is in many ways one of the world's most unique grasses, as well as one of the very best meadow grasses known to man (Fig. 63). It is the most important cultivated grass for hay in the humid northeastern United States, and southward to the Cotton Belt, and westward to near the limit of the Corn Belt. It is also grown in the humid portions of the northern Rocky Mountains and in western Washington and Oregon. Timothy has often been cut for seed in the middle western United States, the annual production of seed being as high as 2,000,000 bushels with a value of about $4,000,000. The states which commonly have furnished most of the timothy seed are Ohio, Illinois, Missouri, and Iowa. The yield of timothy seed in 1945 was 1,306,300 bushels on an acreage of 353,700 acres. Iowa produced 659,000 bushels that year. Large quantities of the seed are exported.

In the Old World timothy is now widely cultivated from the British

Isles to Germany, and to Norway and Sweden where it thrives in the mountain valleys close to the Arctic Circle. The species was first grown as a cultivated hay plant in the United States, rather than in Europe, and it is said to be named after one Mr. Timothy Hanson, an American colonial farmer. Timothy, especially as it is often grown in mixture with red clover, is America's most common hay crop in the matter of the number of farms that grow it, but it is far out-yielded in tons of hay produced by alfalfa.

Numerous other grasses are valuable meadow species over the globe in various mixtures and under various conditions of climate and soil. Thus Orchard Grass, *Dactylis glomerata*, Tall Oat Grass, *Arrhenatherum elatius*, Bent or Redtop, *Agrostis* spp., and Kentucky Bluegrass, *Poa pratensis*, are often seen in meadow culture under conditions that are

Fig. 63. Timothy is probably the most important meadow grass now grown in the United States *(from Hitchcock)*.

more or less similar to those best suited to timothy. Creeping Bent, *Agrostis palustris*, is a valued grass for meadows and pastures in northern Europe.

Cogon Grass, *Imperata cylindrica*, and related species, are widespread relatives of the bluestems which are found mostly in the warmer parts of the world. These are prized as meadow species in various regions where the hay is made when the plants are still quite young.

Various cereals, especially rye and oats and other grasses, are often locally sown for hay in order to supply feed during an unfavorable period or under unfavorable climatic conditions. Certain species of grasses are also of value for hay production under irrigation or under the conditions of naturally wet land. Cereals cut for hay in 1945 yielded 3,667,000 tons.

CHAPTER 12

Grasses in Relation to Soil Conservation

GRASSES AND OTHER GREEN PLANTS DIRECTLY OR INDIRECTLY FURNISH the foods that sustain the life of all animals including man. Such plants could not perform this tremendously significant role were it not for the fact that they are equipped to anchor themselves in the soil and so to receive into their bodies certain essential substances that are available to them only from the soil. The green plant is the only vital intermediary that operates between the richly endowed storehouse of relatively simple nutritive materials that are about it in the soil and air and the complex foods that are demanded by all the varied forms of animal and plant life. These are the main reasons why *soil conservation* is one of the most universal, fundamental, and vital problems of the entire realm of natural science and civilization.

When the soil is mistreated the vegetation, whether natural or highly domesticated, suffers and society is impoverished. The continuation and expansion of this trend ultimately leads to serious deterioration of the soil throughout great areas and may contribute to the destruction of the agriculture and civilization of nations, a truth to which the history of mankind is witness. Assyria, Babylonia, and China furnish startling examples of this fact. Such experiences have been too common through the ages, and are still so close that sensible Americans derive little comfort from the common boast that we have conquered nature.

Man should constantly remember that nature worked for millions of years to block out the climatic patterns of the world, to perfect the substratum of soil, and to cover it with a mantle of prairie or some other type of grassland. The *soil*, the *climate*, and the *grasses* have marched hand in hand through those countless centuries. We must

153

understand that the grasslands of the globe are much more than simply areas of land that are more or less well blanketed with grass. If that green mantle is destroyed by the forces of nature working alone or in conjunction with greedy men, we may never hope to restore it completely. Man must, therefore, do everything that his ingenuity can devise to conserve the soil and its precious cover if they are to continue to yield their indispensable values under the relentless lash of the natural climatic and biological controls.

Fig. 64. An example of spectacular erosion in rather heavy soil in the Bad Lands of northwestern Nebraska. *(Photo by author.)*

The most serious consequence of the lack of soil conservation and the slight recognition of a sensible plan for it stems from the constant tendency of natural forces to gnaw into, move away, deposit, and in other ways disturb the soil. *Erosion* is the word we have for this complex universal phenomenon. The literal meaning of the word is picturesque, but it is also terrifying. The English word *erosion* is derived from the Latin *rodere,* which means *to gnaw,* plus *e,* which means *out* or *away from.* Thus the noun, erosion, means a gnawing away from or a wearing away, as of land or soil by the action of water and wind (Fig. 64). The enormous changes that have occurred in the surface of the earth caused by these mighty processes are viewed with awe. The gnawing began at the surface of the land when the earth was exceedingly young, in fact, as soon as the first land appeared above the sea.

The first chapters of the story of erosion take us, as has been suggested, into the dim mists of the geological past. That was long before the appearance of life on the globe, certainly before the creation of terrestrial life. Science has pieced the story together with sufficient degree of perfection that we now recognize two broad periods or phases of the general phenomenon of erosion. These, in chronological order, are *geological* erosion and *soil* erosion. The one is very old, the other comparatively young, yet both are vigorously progressing under our eyes at this very time. The type of erosion with which we are mainly concerned here is the latter, since it deals primarily with accelerated erosion as caused by human action.

Geological erosion involves the fragmentation and decomposition of great masses of primitive rocks and the scattering and deposition of the mineral materials of which they are composed. These complex natural phenomena are very significant in the early stages of the evolution of the principal land forms of the earth. Canyons, valleys, plateaus, plains, mesas, deltas are formed by these forces. This phase of erosion, obviously, is of great practical value, too, since it is essential to the eventual formation and preparation of the mineral constituents of the soil as the natural substratum of all native vegetation and cultivated crops. The impressive earlier trends of geological erosion in their bolder aspects are noteworthy features of most mountainous areas that are far removed from the influence of man. Laborious and even dangerous hikes over the riven fastness of highland America, Switzerland, and Norway impress man with the might of these tremendous forces at work. Those places offer a miniature of the vivid action that must have operated on a grand scale during an early age as they blocked out the main aspects of the sculptured face of the earth.

Soil erosion eventually follows geological erosion and is related to human interference with the natural processes involved. It especially deals with the conditions that characterize the more or less well-formed soil and its varied biological relationships, including the plant life that in time develops upon the land. The gnawing away and the transportation of the soil by water and wind, and its deposition elsewhere, doubtless occurred with great fury and over wide areas long before natural vegetation developed a resistant cover that effectively pro-

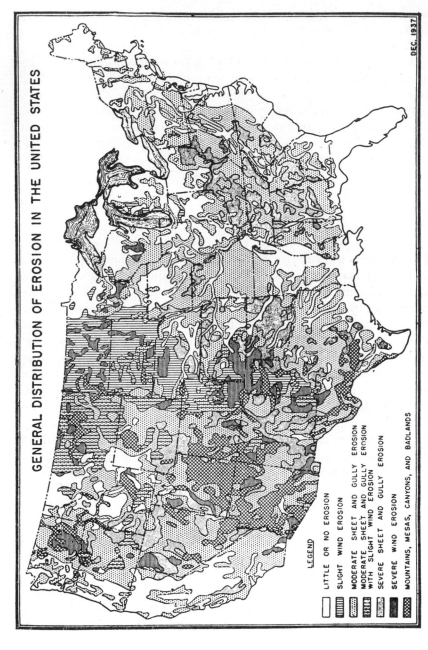

Fig. 65. Erosion map of the United States. This map should hang on the wall of every home. *(Photo from Yearbook of Agriculture, furnished by Soil Conservation Service, U. S. Department of Agriculture.)*

tected the surface. Lightning probably started fires in the world's grasslands and forests long before the entry of man into the story. The natural vegetative cover in such places was so disturbed by this natural hazard that soil erosion, dust storms, and floods occurred with all their destructive features as the natural consequence of the disturbance.

Mankind entered the cycle at a very recent time, as the long history of the earth goes. Early man eventually discovered that it was neces-

Fig. 66. Small gullies caused by melting snow in Maine, may be seen on practically every farm in northern United States. *(Photo from Soil Conservation Service, U. S. Department of Agriculture.)*

sary to break the soil and sod of the grasslands and forests and to remove the natural cover of grasses or trees in order that he could plant and cultivate crops to supplement the meager food supply that he secured from the wilds. The increasing population that accompanied these improvements in the march of civilization could not be fed by recourse to nature's store alone. Domesticated crops and improved breeds of animals necessitated the expansion of an ever increasing area of cultivated land. This could be provided only by

removing the natural cover from larger and larger areas of virgin soil
and thus exposing more and more soil to the potential damage caused
by sweeping winds and by run-off and floods. The rapid removal of
soil that is likely to follow when the cover is removed results in the
deterioration of the land, the reduction of crops, the gulleying of the
fields, and eventually in the complete ruination of productive areas
(Figs. 66, 67). When such destructive forces are allowed to develop over
extensive regions they cause widespread impoverishment of the people
to such a degree as to modify the evolution of society and civilization.
The degeneration and failure of agriculture that accompanies the de-
cline of the land, whatever the cause, is sure to leave its record upon the
history of nations and cultures. Great areas of the ancient lands
including famous cities, are now depopulated and desolate as a result,
in part at least, of severe erosion.

Water and wind are the chief natural forces that gnaw away and
shift about the surface of the soil. Enormous quantities of soil may
be removed and transported to distant regions by these agents. The
results of such natural changes are extremely variable as they operate
on different kinds of soils and slopes and under different climatic conditions and with different kinds of vegetational cover. The progressive action of erosion has been greatly accelerated in the past by the
management of the land. This glaring fact has lately suggested that
man may expect great success in the control of erosion by a modification of his attitude toward the soil and the adoption of a broad-scale
land management with that objective definitely in mind.

Vast acreages of the Old World and of the United States (Fig. 65)
have already been ruined or seriously damaged by erosion. The damage
continues in spite of all that man has done in his effort to stop or
control it. The Soil Conservation Service of the United States Department of Agriculture has estimated that the annual monetary cost of
erosion in this country is at least $400,000,000 in terms of lost produc-
tivity alone. This would accumulate to $20,000,000,000 in fifty years.
To these astounding figures must be added the huge losses caused by
various other features of the dreadful story that involves every living
being. The same governmental agency estimates that 282,000,000
acres of land have been ruined or severely damaged, and that 775,-
000,000 acres have been moderately damaged, that 50,000,000 acres of
crop land have been ruined, and that an additional 50,000,000 acres
of *crop land* have been severely damaged. Added to this frightening
situation is the further statement that from one-half to all of the top

soil has been removed from 100,000,000 acres, and that the destructive processes of erosion have already begun on an additional 100,000,000 acres! The rate at which these changes are occurring is also disturbing. These are startling changes and figures. They indicate not only the amazing enormity of past and current erosion in this fair young country, but also that this situation is a major threat to the continuous prosperity of the nation. If the future is viewed in terms of the horrors of this past, unbounded enthusiasm for and support of the nation-wide program of soil conservation is greatly needed.

Fig. 67. Deep gulleying of valuable pasture land in a mountain park in Colorado. *(Photo by author.)*

USES OF GRASSES TO CONTROL EROSION

The facts and some of the obvious dangers of soil erosion have been known to observant men since ancient times. The more attentive farmers and foresters of later centuries as well as others who have been close to the land, have long recognized the damage done by erosion, and have made attempts to protect their lands. The great American, Patrick Henry, once declared that the greatest patriot is the one who stops the most gullies. For many decades, however, about all that was done to stop the formation of gullies in the United States was to dump refuse such as straw and brush or garbage into them, perhaps with the careless hope that erosion would somehow be stopped and the sharp depressions would be filled with soil that was continually washed down from the surrounding land. Little thought was given to the possible treatment of the upper slopes or the places where the damage really begins. Terracing was later employed, but in a similar isolated and haphazard manner for many years. Contour tillage, crop rotation, and strip cropping all came in for some attention as the progressive destruction became more and more extensive and impressive. Rapidly increasing erosion called for more attention to the serious consequences involved and, so, many states finally began to devote serious thought to the problems of soil conservation.

The threat of the gulley had to become more widespread and better known to more people, however, before the nation gave its approval to the formation of a technical federal organization to attack the erosion problem on a national scope. This great research organization was set up only in 1935, and it is now known as the Soil Conservation Service of the United States Department of Agriculture, U.S.S.C.S. for short. This significant agency has entered into a nation-wide program of intensive investigation of the problems of soil erosion and soil conservation in general. The federal government has in this way also attacked the

Fig. 68. American Beach Grass, a species that is naturally adapted to sandy soils and is effectively planted to stabilize such places *(after Hitchcock)*.

broad questions of soil conservation in close cooperation with our individual states.

The local studies made by the various states and the extensive and detailed researches by the U.S.S.C.S. in its first decade have clearly demonstrated that erosion can be controlled. The most valuable, natural, and sensible methods for reducing the menace of soil erosion involve the careful management of the cover of native vegetation and introduced plants and cultivated crops that are present or that may be available.

In short, the best control over soil erosion is to protect the soil, especially on the upper slopes, from reaching a condition that permits erosion. A cover consisting of forest trees and shrubs is effective in reducing erosion and run-off. They are used to reforest cutover areas, abandoned fields, and various types of submarginal lands. A dense natural cover of grasses guards against erosion on the range, in the

Fig. 69. Contour strip cropping on a 37 per cent slope. This suggests essential management on such steep slopes and in such corn fields. The rows should be on exact contours. *(Photo from Soil Conservation Service, U. S. Department of Agriculture.)*

pasture and in the meadow. A firm cover of introduced or native grasses and other cultivated crops likewise protects the soil in tilled fields and gardens. But the management of all these areas must be so planned as to control and maintain the proper cover and in other ways to reduce the exposure to erosion if we wish to control that danger.

This control, as applied to grassland, includes such more or less natural practices in the management of livestock as herding control, rotation grazing, and deferred grazing, as practiced in the range and pasture. Artificial seeding with indigenous or introduced species is always an alluring possibility in connection with these measures. The other ways of soil conservation include the use and perfection of contouring, terracing, crop rotation, strip cropping, seasonal cover crops, and the use of crop residues, especially as available in the management of cultivated crops on the tilled land of farms (Fig. 69).

The use of certain impressive engineering features such as dams, dikes, ditches, and the construction of artificial channels and outlets may also be used to advantage in the prevention of soil erosion. It may be observed with reference to the latter devices that such works should be unnecessary if proper controls were perfected on the slopes of the fields and forests and over the watersheds in general.

Many of the methods that are directed toward soil conservation by means of erosion control may also be used in the conservation of *wild life* in general as well as for those purposes that are more intimately and abundantly related to man's direct use of the land. Preliminary success in these directions is encouraging.

GRASSES AID IN CONTROL

The species of grasses which quickly develop a thick or resistant cover are of great value in holding the soil against the initial damage that is caused by the erosive forces. The grassy cover tends to break the force of falling rain, to absorb the precipitation, and to hold the surface of the soil in position. In this manner the grasses operate to reduce run-off, to check the formation and deepening of gullies, reduce the constant deterioration of land, and so to simplify the difficulty of land management. The myriads of slender, thread-like, fibrous roots firmly anchor the grasses in the soil and at the same time they bind the particles of the soil together far beneath the surface. The cover of leaves and stems breaks the mechanical effect of the falling rain drops and aids in the interception of the rain and in this way greatly reduces the initial beating of the surface of the soil and the dashing and washing effect of the rain. All these influences make it possible for the water to soak into the soil more deliberately and completely. Thus the grasses effectively contribute, in a perfectly *natural* way, to soil conservation by preventing or reducing erosion by means of their inherent habits—*if* they are only given a fair chance.

Many species of true grasses are of great value for the prevention or control of erosion when growing alone or in mixture or in combination with other close-growing plants that are not grasses. These grow naturally over the range and in the pastures and meadows or they may be used under the highly artificial seeding management of ranges and cultivated farm lands. Scores of such species, including both native and exotic plants, have been culled from the flora of the world and are being tried by various countries in extensive experimentation with the hope of developing more effective measures for the control of soil erosion in various portions of our country and the world.

Grasses that are effective against erosion under the natural conditions of our semiarid and arid western range include many of the species that are indigenous to that region and certain exotic species as well. Some of the better known plants of this group may be indicated in the following list:

Buffalo Grass, *Buchloë dactyloides*
Blue Grama, *Bouteloua gracilis*
Side-oats Grama, *Bouteloua curtipendula*
Black Grama, *Bouteloua eripoda*
Hairy Grama, *Bouteloua hirsuta*
Western Wheat Grass, *Agropyron smithii*
Crested Wheat Grass, *Agropyron cristatum*
Blue-bunch Wheat Grass, *Agropyron spicatum*
Curly Mesquite, *Hilaria belangeri*
Little Bluestem, *Andropogon scoparius*
Big Bluestem, *Andropogon furcatus*
Silver Beard-grass, *Andropogon saccharoides*
Canada Wild Rye, *Elymus canadensis*
Beardless Wild Rye, *Elymus triticoides*
Galleta Grass, *Hilaria jamesii*
Tabosa Grass, *Hilaria mutica*
Needle Grass, *Stipa spartea*

The most of the above species form good to very tough sods or they grow in bunches. Some of them are also more or less drought-resistant, and therefore admirably adapted to erosion control on the drier parts of the range. Many of the species are excellent for the control of gulleys in the range, especially when they develop a maximum cover on the slopes. Under such conditions gullies do not even get started.

Species of grasses that have been effective in man's effort to control erosion particularly in gulleys that are already formed under various conditions, include Bermuda Grass, *Cynodon dactylon*, Kentucky Blue-grass, *Poa pratensis*, Silver Beard-grass, *Andropogon saccharoides*, Little Bluestem, *Andropogon scoparius*, and Buffalo Grass, *Buchloë dactyloides*. These grasses are introduced in the form of sods or tufts, from which new growth spreads until a cover is established and further erosion is prevented.

GRASSES OF SANDY SOILS

The problem of wind erosion, especially in sandy soils (Fig. 70) and in arid regions, is likely to be more impressive at the moment than the steady erosion by water. A district whose dominant feature is an extensive, restless maze of naked, wandering sand dunes is one of earth's most interesting and dynamic environments. The spectacular results of water erosion are, however, often the most impressive features of the landscape in arid regions, strange as that may seem. The *common*

Fig. 70. Effects of wind erosion on range land in sandy soil in Nebraska. *(Photo by the author.)*

types of water erosion are more widely spread, continuous, and unimpressive but nevertheless very insidious. Frequent dust storms and occasional "black blizzards" serve to force upon us the serious consequences of baring the soil to the wind (Fig. 71), whatever may be the reason for the mismanagement that severely reduces the ground-cover of vegetation.

Soil particles in finely divided state may be blown for thousands of miles. Scores of tons of soil per square mile may be picked up and deposited over distant regions during a single wind storm. Soil from the prairie region of the United States was blown over the eastern states and out on the Atlantic Ocean during the dust storms of the 1930's. Tons of finely divided soil may be suspended in the atmosphere over a given area in such "dust bowls" during such storms so as to produce an effect of twilight at mid-day. Fields may be completely denuded by the wind and the soil cut away for many inches beneath the original surface (Fig. 71). Other fields close by or at a distance are often covered with soil that is freshly deposited from the air during such storms. Buildings, pastures, and gardens about farm homes (Fig. 72) and in the towns are damaged by the deposit that was carried in by the wind. The direct economic losses and the suffering and unrest imposed upon people by dust storms may be severe throughout large areas during periods of prolonged drought.

The best measures for the prevention and control of wind erosion, as for water erosion, employ methods of management that guard the soil against the breakage of the ground cover and other conditions that present an opening for direct attack by the wind. If the cover has been opened by fire, overgrazing, or cultivation in regions and soils that are subject to wind erosion, then strenuous efforts may be necessary to prevent great damage to the soil and to the economic and social values of the territory so afflicted.

Fig. 71. The advancing front of a dust storm; the storm lasted about three hours, under a wind velocity of approximately 30 miles per hour. *(Photo from Soil Conservation Service, U. S. Department of Agriculture.)*

The stabilization and eventual recovery of wind-swept lands may be accomplished by the encouragement of the natural cover, or by the artificial introduction of grasses or certain other plants and the subsequent development of a new resistant cover.   Forest trees have been successfully planted in certain windy areas to accomplish this end, as in the Landes of France and in the sandhills of Nebraska.   The sandy soil in both of these regions had been fairly well fixed by the growth of grasses before the trees were planted.   The initial cover that was furnished by the grasses provided the important degree of protection without which the establishment of the forests could not have succeeded.

The recovery of range grassland in which wind has caused serious damage may often be readily and simply effected by keeping the livestock out for a time.   The early invasion and the final establishment of grasses in such exposed areas is known to be readily accomplished in many places over our own western range lands and in Australia.

Certain species of the grasses that commonly and naturally occur within wind-swept grasslands quickly let their presence be known, following the simplest consideration by the owners of such lands. They will soon clothe the unstable soil with a resistant cover if they are given half a chance, and from then on conditions will improve, even in the very face of the wind.

The following list includes some of the better known species of grasses that have been used or that may be used for the natural control and management of wind-blown soils especially where the soil is very sandy:

Sand Reed-grass, *Calamovilfa longifolia*
Giant Sand Reed-grass, *Calamovilfa gigantea*
Blowout Grass, *Redfieldia flexuosa*

American Beach Grass, *Ammophila brevilgulata*
Western Dune Grass, *Elymus arenicola and E. flavescens*
Marram or European Dune Grass, *Ammophila arenaria*
Dune Grass, *Elymus mollis*
Sea Oats-grass, *Uniola paniculata*

Muhly Dune Grass, *Muhlenbergia pungens*
Needle-and-thread Grass, *Stipa comata*
Indian Rice Grass, *Oryzopsis hymenoides*
Littleseed Rice Grass, *Oryzopsis micrantha*
Sanddune Panic Grass, *Panicum amarum*
Sand Dropseed, *Sporobolus cryptandrus*
Nevada Bluegrass, *Poa nevadensis*
Sandhill Lovegrass, *Eragrostis trichodes*

A noteworthy grass has been used in the Old World for erosion control in sandy areas, especially in France, the Netherlands, Denmark, and Germany. This is European Dune Grass or Marram Grass, *Ammophila arenaria.* This species is a very close relative of our American Beach Grass, *A. breviligulata.* The latter (Fig. 68) has been planted with success in the sandy wastes of Cape Cod and the Golden Gate. The forests of maritime pine, *Pinus maritima,* of Bordeau were established in the dune areas there after the blowing of the soil had been partially arrested by the planting of the Marram Dune Grass. It was from those forests that American soldiers, who were trained and ex-

FIG. 72. An abandoned farm home in the "dust bowl" of the North American prairie, showing the disastrous effects of wind erosion. *(Photo from Soil Conservation Service, U. S. Department of Agriculture.)*

perienced in technical forestry, secured much of the timber that was necessary to prepare for the landing and operation of General Pershing's armies in France during World War I.

Considerable work has been done in Australia in the effort to reduce the severe losses from soil erosion, especially in sandy soils. The grasses that have been used for such purposes in Australia include the so-called Porcupine Grasses, *Spinifex hirsutus* and *S. paradoxus.*

Overgrazing and other phases of poor management have resulted in much wind erosion and severe damage over some of the great ranches or *estancias* of the Argentinian pampa. Wide areas have been involved in this situation and huge belts of shifting soils have been developed in several localities. The Argentine government has endeavored to correct these destructive tendencies by planting Marram Grass, *Ammophila arenaria,* on the eroding soils. General Smuts, former premier of the Union of West Africa, has declared that erosion is one of the most fundamental and serious problems of Africa.

One of the features of soil erosion which has lately received increasing attention is the fact that the process carries away or depletes the soil of certain mineral nutrients without which our crop and garden plants do not develop normally. The quantity of such nutrients in the parts of the plants used as food may be so reduced as to lead to malnutrition, or at least to an undernourished condition in human beings and livestock. Thus a relatively insidious influence may in time affect the health and life of a nation which tolerates soil erosion.

Students of human nutrition state that about two-thirds of the population of the earth are more or less continually undernourished. We might reduce this terrible condition by giving more thought and action to the evils of erosion on a national and international scale. Let us give our *grasses* a chance to aid in this important matter!

CHAPTER 13

Grasses for Lawns, Parks and Playing Fields

WHEN CIVILIZATION REACHED THE MORE FAVORABLE COOLER AND LESS humid intermediate climates beyond the tropical rain forests and, especially, when men abandoned their wandering nomadic life to settle down in a more or less permanent abode in villages and small towns, they missed the green mantle of the wild grassy landscape. They probably tended to satisfy this longing by transplanting certain wild grasses to the village. The extended introduction of certain grasses close about the homes and in public parks and playgrounds for the sheer beauty of the greensward rather than for pasture or range has been the result of man's eternal quest for beauty. The movement has gone so far in our time that a new home, be it in a side street and ever so humble or a mansion on the boulevard, is now no sooner under way than detailed plans are made for the lawn.

Grassy parks of surpassing beauty and well-grassed playing fields are features of the urban life of many countries. Americans are especially conscious of the values associated with a fine, well-kept lawn about the home. Much of the effort that we devote to lawn culture in this country is, unfortunately, poorly rewarded because of lack of attention to the many complex problems involved. The successful lawn enthusiast makes constant use of the best information available in this highly specialized and technical phase of grass culture.

The lawns, parks, playing plots, golf courses, and other recreation grounds of the world represent an enormous acreage in the aggregate. There are probably more than twenty million home lawns in the United States. In addition there are hundreds of schools, colleges and other private and public institutions that greatly extend these uses of grasses. All of this represents a financial outlay that qualifies as big

169

business. It has been estimated, for example, that there are about 3,000 golf courses in the northeastern quarter of the United States and that the annual maintenance cost alone of these totals at least $45,-000,000.

It is not the purpose of this book to present even an introductory treatment of the many problems involved in the establishment and maintenance of the grassy cover for the lawn, park, or recreation plot. Only brief notes upon a few of the more prominent grasses that are known to be successfully used for such purposes in various parts of the world are to be included.

The qualities demanded of the grasses that are to be used for lawns and parks are more or less summed up in the expression *turf-formers*. The word *turf* is applied to the shallow, upper layer of soil and vegetable mould that is finely permeated by the fibrous roots of grasses so as to form a sort of tough *mat, sward,* or *sod*. The turf grasses, therefore, are those that best contribute to the development and persistence of this condition. Many such species present unusual *aerial* characteristics that are also demanded in popular lawn grasses.

One may readily understand that grasses which are of high value for forage, hay, or grain would be useless for lawns or bowling greens because of their relatively poor turf-forming qualities or because of the fact that they are too coarse or tall. Only the lower, finer-stemmed grasses are likely to be popular for these purposes. The fine texture that is so desirable in a grass ideally suited for a bowling green would not be so good for the rigorous play of the football gridiron or hockey pitch where the harder, tough species would certainly be preferred. The perennial species of good color that normally produce numerous fine stems and leaves which develop and remain close to the ground and that will stand frequent mowing and trampling are the best for such uses. There is a fair range of choice among the grasses of this kind that are adapted to various climates and soils and for the special uses that may be involved. Some will thrive in light, dry, sandy soils, others only under more humid climate and moist, firm soils.

The species of grasses that are of most importance for these purposes are included in three large genera of world-wide distribution. These are the Bluegrasses, which are species of the genus *Poa*, the Bent Grasses, species of *Agrostis,* and the Fescue Grasses, which belong to the genus *Festuca*.

Of the numerous species included in *Poa* the so-called Kentucky Bluegrass, *Poa pratensis* (Fig. 58), is probably the one that is most widely known and used for lawns and parks. This species has already been mentioned in this book as an important grass for meadows and pastures. This European species is our best lawn grass, in general, for the northern United States, where the weather does not get too dry or too hot and where an abundance of supplementary water is available. It does not do well in shade or when it is cut too short by the lawn mower. Kentucky Bluegrass will survive periods of rather high temperature and dry weather in a dormant state, after the sod is well established.

The Rough Bluegrass, *P. trivialis,* will endure much more shade than will the above species, but is not so good for the northern as for the warmer southern states. This species is widely used in the Old World, as in England, for shady areas and cold, wet soils that are kept well fertilized.

Canada Bluegrass, *Poa compressa,* is frequently used in the northern and eastern United States where it fares better than does Kentucky Bluegrass in poor, dry soils.

The European lawn makers often use the Wood Bluegrass, *Poa nemoralis,* for lawns, especially where adaptation to shade is demanded. This species was introduced from Europe into North America where it is grown in southeastern Canada and the northeastern United States.

The Annual Bluegrass, *P. annua,* thrives fairly well as a lawn grass in the warmer parts of the United States, but elsewhere it is likely to become a troublesome weed in the lawn. The abundant seeding habits of this species and its endurance of poor soils and unfavorable weather conditions enables it to form a good turf in the fall and spring where other lawn plants would fail.

The Bent Grasses, which are various species of *Agrostis* (Fig. 73) are popular for lawns and putting greens because of their fine texture. These are called "bent grasses" because of the habit of growth of the stems, especially when they are not crowded. The stems tend to grow along the surface of the ground for a variable distance and then turn or bend upward.

Creeping Bent is the common name for the prominent species, *Agrostis stolonifera,* which is widely spread across the northern United States and Europe. The extensively creeping surface stems or *stolons* which take root at the joints are a striking feature of this grass. Several varieties of this species are recognized by the experts and they are highly recommended and widely used for the putting greens of golf courses. The fine-textured, springy turf of Creeping Bent that is produced in response to close and frequent mowing and top dressing is greatly enjoyed by the golfer when he steps up to the edge of the putting green and tries to "sink a long one" that is, if he *really* does *sink* it. With the poor care and treatment bestowed upon the average lawn Creeping Bent is not so good as a lawn grass. It does not do well in the shade. The ordinary property owner will not and cannot devote the time that is necessary to maintain a good lawn with this species.

FIG. 73. Redtop, a grass that is closely related to the famous Creeping Bent *(from Hitchcock)*.

Colonial Bent, *A. tenuis,* is another grass that is good for open, not shady, lawns in the northern portions of Europe and the United States. It develops a very fine, dense, *velvety* greensward under the constant clipping of the putting green. This species is often mixed with other grasses in the management of lawns even under a wide variety of soil conditions.

Velvet Bent, *Agrostis canina,* also a native of Europe, has been introduced into the northeastern United States and is another very popular species for putting greens. It is more readily adapted to the drier regions since it is rather tolerant of both heat and cold, and does well under shade and in the open. The lawn or green of Velvet Bent may be kept closely clipped, and under such treatment the grass develops many short stolons or creeping stems and myriads of short, fine, narrow leaves. Thus the green "velvety" turf so produced reflects the common name for the species. Several distinct varieties of the species have been developed by grass-greens specialists. Certain of these, when in pure stands or in mixture with other grasses, are used in the maintenance of many of the most famous putting greens, bowling greens, lawns, and parks in the world.

The third main group of grasses that are used for these purposes includes several species that are widely known as Fescue Grasses. The generic name is *Festuca,* an ancient Latin name that was applied to a weedy grass. We have already noted that many of the perennial species of *Festuca* are important forage grasses on the western range, while others, such as *F. elatior,* the Meadow Fescue of Europe, and Sheep's Fescue, *F. ovina,* are used for hay and pasture. Several of the fescues are ideally adapted to lawn, putting green, bowling green, and parkway uses.

Red Fescue, *Festuca rubra* (Fig. 74) is widely distributed in North America, Europe, and Africa. Numerous varieties have been recognized by the specialists. Several of these are highly prized for putting greens and bowling greens. They are useful under a wide variety of conditions of soil and climate, from dry upland sand to peaty moors near the sea coast. The numerous dwarf stems and fine leaves of Red Fescue that quickly respond to close mowing and top dressing are features that contribute to its well established reputation. One of the varieties of this species that is known as Chewing's Fescue was brought to the United States from New Zealand and it has become popular as a lawn grass in the north, especially when used in mixture with certain other grasses. The regular form of Red Fescue, *F. rubra,* is very popular in Europe where the closely cropped,

FIG. 74. Red Fescue, one of the best of a famous genus of American and European grasses *(from Hitchcock).*

fine, wiry foliage is often seen on golf courses and in the parks.

Sheep's Fescue, *Festuca ovina,* is a popular grass for poor, thin soils where it is able to maintain itself and provide a cover where other species would fail. Some of the principal places where these values are secured are on golf links in the British Isles where the soil is light and poor, as over the seaside golf courses and the heather-clad moors. The varieties of Sheep's Fescue, known as Hard Fescue, *duriuscula,* and Fine-leaved Fescue, *tenuifolia,* are highly prized for such rather unfavorable situations at home and abroad. Hard Fescue, *Festuca durius-*

cula, is said to be very drought-resistent and to adapt itself to the conditions peculiar to hillsides, and in gravel, sand, or chalky soils.

Another noteworthy lawn grass that marched with man from the Old World to the United States is Bermuda Grass, *Cynodon dactylon* (Fig. 60). This species is widely grown as a lawn grass in the southern states, where in fact it plays the same role as that taken by Kentucky Bluegrass in the northern states. The warm humid climate of the south favors Bermuda Grass and repels Kentucky Bluegrass. Bermuda Grass is as much of importance as a pasture grass in the south as is Kentucky Bluegrass in the north. These two grasses are very different in their generic and specific characters and in their climatic requirements, but they are very similar in their contributions to mankind.

Manila Grass, *Zoysia matrella,* is said to be an ideal lawn grass for many tropical areas. This species has been given a thorough trial at the Puerto Rican Experiment Station where it does well even in dry, hot weather. It remains green during dry weather and it repels many weeds. This species also withstands considerable shade, which is an especially desirable quality. It is good for lawns, play grounds, roadways, golf tees, fairways, and cemeteries, as well as for football fields and drill grounds. The toughness of the stems and leaves make it hard to cut by the usual hand lawn mower, but the motor-driven rotary mower cuts it very easily. Although this species is most useful in tropical and subtropical countries, it has been successful in temperate or intermediate climates, as in the United States as far north as Connecticut. The closely related *Zoysia tenuifolia,* which is known as Mascarene Grass and Korean Velvet Grass, is grown to some extent in Florida and California.

The problems that are involved in establishing and maintaining good lawns in the semiarid and arid sections of the world are often greatly intensified by the soil types and climatic conditions that prevail in such places. The people on the large ranches and farms of the broad country districts where these conditions prevail are most commonly content with the more or less scanty growth of the local grasses about the home. Less commonly, in places where an adequate supply of supplemental water is available, they often try out various lawn grasses that would not otherwise endure the natural conditions. Given the necessary materials, time, and labor, such efforts will often yield amazing results even in the most severely arid environment. This is revealed in many towns and cities of the arid regions of the world.

Of the various local grasses that are of some value for parks and playing fields under arid conditions we may mention the native American Buffalo Grass, *Buchloë dactyloides.* This famous North American species (Fig. 10) produces a turf of unusual toughness and tenacity as was demonstrated by its wide use for the sod houses of the pioneers who first settled on the American prairies. The low, fine, kinky growth of stems and foliage endures the tramping to which it is exposed in the lawns and parks and over the golf links of its natural range. Buffalo Grass does not make the smooth even lawn that is easily kept by frequent mowing as do many of the other grasses mentioned, and the rather dull grayish color of such a lawn is not regarded as the best. Another objectionable feature of Buffalo Grass when used for lawns is that it is late in its development in spring and it becomes more or less dry and yellow early in the fall. Its season as a lawn grass is relatively short as compared with the more popular species preferred for lawns.

Various other grasses of unusual nature are used for lawns under special local conditions in certain countries. Thus the Cogon Grass or Siru, *Imperata cylindrica,* which is usually a tall coarse grass of tropical savannas, is used in its depauperate form as a lawn grass in northern India.

Several different species of less valuable grasses for the lawn are often sown in mixture with the best turf grasses in the establishment of new lawns, putting greens, and parks. These are usually temporary, quickly growing forms that more or less protect the slower growing permanent species. They aid in checking erosion, and in various ways assist the principal turf-forming grasses to establish themselves. These temporary grasses are commonly known as *nurse* grasses. Such grasses are usually somewhat coarser and taller than the permanent turf-formers, and they tend to produce a more open stand and looser sod. Such species really do aid the more delicate grasses to get off to a better start under the rather precarious conditions that exist at the surface level of a new lawn or green. The nurse grasses eventually give way to the permanent sod formers as the latter become thicker and denser and as the area is clipped and dressed in passing into its regular or permanent scheme of management.

Several species are used as nurse grasses and these serve to meet the conditions peculiar to different parts of the world. The Redtop, *Agrostis alba* (Fig. 73), a grass that is often used for meadows and pastures in America and elsewhere, is one of these. Other nurse grasses are Meadow Fescue, *Festuca pratensis,* and Perennial Ryegrass, *Lolium perenne.* These are useful in various mixtures and under various conditions of soil and climate. Certain other species, such as Meadow Foxtail, *Alopecurus pratensis,* Crested Dogstail Grass, *Cynosurus cristatus,* and Sweet Vernal Grass, *Anthoxanthum odoratum,* are used as nurse grasses in Europe. Even such tall, coarse pasture and meadow species as Smooth Brome Grass, *Bromus inermis* (Fig. 61), Timothy, *Phleum pratense* (Fig. 63), and Orchard Grass, *Dactylis glomerata* (Fig. 59), are sometimes used as nurses. The latter species must not be allowed to develop very far or they may become so tall, bunchy, and coarse as to defeat the purpose for which they are used turning the plot into a meadow or pasture rather than a lawn. Such coarser grasses are often used abroad, along with Kentucky Bluegrass for football fields and hockey pitches, and on the fairways of golf courses.

CHAPTER 14

Miscellaneous Interests in Grasses

THE GRASSES CONTRIBUTE A SURPRISINGLY VARIED AND NUMEROUS SERIES of values and interests to mankind in addition to those outstanding major contributions and better known relationships that have been considered in the preceding chapters. When the Beau Brummel of main street flashes forth in early summer with his clean, new *straw* hat, and when the irrepressible fisherman on the trout stream smears his face and neck with his favorite "skeeter scoot" composed of *citronella* oil, we recognize some of these contributions. Likewise, when the home owner struggles valiantly and almost hopelessly to eradicate the strangling "water grass" from his lawn, we understand that grasses, in contrast to all their major good and essential qualities, may sometimes be extremely troublesome and undesirable.

There are few grasses that are lacking in the beauty of foliage and flower. The fundamental greenness of their foliage is one of the most common major aspects of the landscape. When we combine that fact with all the essential biological and social relationships that are involved, we face one of the most profound aspects of the world. Yes, there is beauty, there is poetry in grasses, as is amply revealed by the thoughts of many of the world's great writers. There are many species of grasses that are of widespread popular value because of the beauty of certain more or less unique or extreme features of foliage and flower.

Some of the more prominent ornamentals among the grasses are those commonly known as the *plume* grasses. The so-called Pampas Grass, *Cortaderia selloana,* a native of the mountain regions of Brazil, Argentina, and Chile is one of the most famous of these. The graceful bunches of drooping leaves of this coarse grass coupled with the dozen or more spectacular flowering shoots are conspicuous in many parks and private estates throughout the tropics. The enormous, graceful plumose clusters of silvery white or pink spikelets borne at the tops of

the stems are the most highly prized feature of this ornamental. The
Eulalia, *Miscanthus sinensis* (Fig. 77), a native of eastern Asia, the
Plume Grass, or Ravenna Grass, *Erianthus ravennae,* of the Mediter-
ranean, and the Giant Reed, *Arundo donax* (Fig. 75), also of the
Mediterranean, are more or less similar grasses that attract the atten-
tion of visitors in our parks and gardens. The tall, beautifully colored

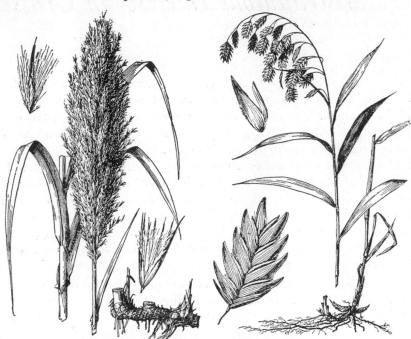

FIG. 75. The Giant Reed whose ornamental value lies mainly in the large
showy panicle or cluster of spikelets
at the top of the stem *(from Hitchcock).*

FIG. 76. Uniola, a grass whose ornamental
quality is seen in the graceful panicles
and large, very flat spikelets *(from
Hitchcock).*

Fountain Grass, *Pennisetum ruppelii,* is often used as a border for
large flower beds. The tall silvery panicles of Cogon Grass, *Imperata
cylindrica,* make fine bouquets. This grass is also used in the marriage
ceremonies of certain castes in India.

The flowering clusters of various grasses make very fine and more
or less distinctive table decorations when arranged in a vase or bowl.
The graceful panicles of various species of Bluegrass, *Poa,* Lovegrass,
Eragrostis, Brome Grass, *Bromus,* Fescue, *Festuca,* Redtop, *Agrostis,*
Quaking Grass, *Briza,* Hairgrass, *Deschampsia,* and Sea Oats, *Uniola*

(Fig. 77), may be mentioned as illustrating the more attractive grasses for this purpose. A species of Quaking Grass, *Briza maxima,* produces spikelets that are pale bronze. The flowers of other grasses are often artificially colored to suit the particular fancy. The stricter spikes of Timothy, *Phleum,* Wheat, *Triticum,* and Barley, *Hordeum,* as well as many others make attractive additions to various types of floral pieces for the table. The beautiful coat-of-arms of the Union of Soviet So-

cialist Republics, as well as the individual seals of the sixteen different Soviet Republics all feature heads of grasses, mostly wheat. Large sheaves or bundles of wheat and other cereals lend themselves to a very attractive degree to the make-up of large pieces for the window, hallway, stage, and public rooms. These are especially fine when used in connection with the decorations for harvest festivals, Thanksgiving, and similar occasions. There is no more typical or orthodox decoration on a large scale for the Thanksgiving season in America than the use of corn stalks and fodder in the shock.

The millinery business sometimes utilizes the decorative value of grasses in the trimming of ladies' hats. At times when this practice has been in style, we

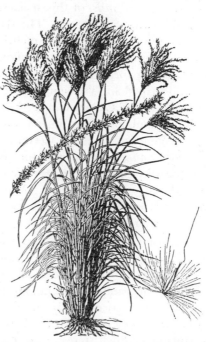

FIG. 77. Eulalia, this large grass with numerous, bushy panicles of myriads of silky spikelets is a very popular ornamental *(from Hitchcock).*

have often identified as many as a dozen or more species of grasses on the spring hats in the Easter parade. The tufts of grasses that are used for these purposes are often artificially colored in order to meet the desired color combinations.

There are several species of grasses that are prized because of their peculiar foliage, such as some of the larger leaved Panic Grasses, *Panicum latifolium, P. boscii,* and *P. clandestinum.* Certain species of Bluestems (Figs. 7, 8) of our American prairies may be mentioned in this connection, especially *Andropogon scoparius* and *A. furcatus,* that add their beautiful shades of purple to the upland and lowland prairie respectively in winter. The odd Ribbon Grass, *Phalaris arundinacea,* var. *picta,* is odd because of the leaves that are striped with white. There are varieties of Eulalia, *Miscanthus sinensis,* with variegated leaves, such as var. *zebrinus,* in which the leaves are cross-banded in white, and the var. *variegatus,* with longitudinally striped leaves. The var. *gracillimus,* of this species, has very narrow leaves which are striped in white and green. The Basket Grass of the American tropics, *Oplismenus hirtellus,* may be mentioned in this connection. This grass is used by florists for edging of flower beds and as a drooping basket plant, largely for its leaves that are striped with pink and white. There are also striped and variegated varieties of Orchard Grass, Sweet Vernal Grass, and Reed Canary Grass.

The bamboos, those giants among the grasses, are commonly of high ornamental quality. Certain species, such as the Dwarf Bamboo, *Bambusa nana,* which is used for hedges in warm, humid climates, and the spreading, *Sasa japonica,* which is a hardy grass that is widely used in parks may be mentioned. Many of the larger tree-like bamboos, when growing singly or in groups, are often striking features of tropical parks and botanical gardens.

Exclusive of sugar cane and the other food-producing grasses, the cereals, there are many other grasses that furnish certain distinctive materials that are of considerable value in the industrial arts and commerce. The bamboos are among the most useful grasses in this connection. The great woody culms of certain species of bamboo are so strong that they are often used in Asia in the construction of houses and bridges. Such stems are often split and the strips then flattened into useful boards. Chinese joss sticks are made of split bamboo. Water mains are made from the stems of bamboos by removing the woody transverse partitions that occur at the nodes. Segments of the stems with intact partitions at the base, and open above serve as useful containers for liquids and solid materials. Implements for farm and garden and household utensils and furniture in great variety are made from the bamboos by the people of Malay lands. Fishing rods and walking sticks that are used in every land are often made from the tough slender stems of bamboos. The tender, crisp young tips of the shoots of various species of bamboo furnish a favorite vegetable food for the Orientals. The flexible, durable strips of bamboo stems are woven into mats, screens, and a great variety of boxes, baskets, and the like. Bangkok hats are made from bamboo. On the whole the bamboos are among the most useful of all grasses.

Rice straw is used in enormous quantity in Japan and China for matting and for wrapping for articles of commerce that are to be shipped. Leghorn hats are made from wheat straw that is cut and bleached when young. Other straw hats are made from oat straw. The real Panama hats are made from the leaves of a South American Palm, *Carludovica palmata*. The palms are *not* grasses.

Two grasses are often used for the fabrication of brooms and coarse brushes. These are Broomcorn, a variety of sorghum, *Sorghum vulgare,* var. *technicum,* and the Broomroot or Mexican Whisk, *Epicampes macroura.* The large bushy inflorescence is used in the former, but in the latter the fibrous roots are bound together to make the coarse brush or broom.

Certain species of grasses are included among textile plants. The most important of these are Esparto, and Alfa, the stems and leaves of which are used for fine paper and cordage. Esparto, *Stipa tenacissima,* and Alfa, *Lygeum spartum,* are both native grasses of North Africa and Spain. It may be noted in passing that Esparto is a close relative of our valuable North American Prairie Grass, *Stipa spartea* (Fig. 9), commonly known as *needle* grass. Cogon Grass, *Imperata cylindrica,* a species of wide distribution in the humid climate of the southwest Pacific and southeastern Asia from Malaya to China and India, has been found to be quite satisfactory for the manufacture of paper. Little has been done, however, to commercialize the species for this purpose. It is reported that the leaves and stems of a Mexican grass known as Broomroot, *Epicampes macroura,* are used for the manufacture of paper. Useful ropes were made from certain native grasses by the American Indians.

The sweet-scented leaves of a few grasses, such as Vanilla Grass, *Hierochloë odorata,* and Sweet Vernal Grass, *Anthoxanthum odoratum,* are used for baskets or covers for baskets, toilet boxes, and cases, or to line such articles. The sweet, vanilla-like odor of the grasses used for such articles gives them a quality that is more or less popular.

The fragrance of the above aromatic grasses suggests other grasses that furnish certain highly scented essential oils which are widely used in perfumery, and in the processing of various cosmetics and drugs. The more common of these important grasses are Citronella Grass, *Cymbopogon nardus,* Lemon Grass, *Cymbopogon citratus,* and Vetiver, *Vetiveria zizanioides.* Citronella oil comes mostly from Java and

Ceylon where the particular grass is extensively cultivated. Lemon oil is secured from the plant that is cultivated in India and Ceylon. This aromatic oil is widely used in perfumery, medicine, and toilet soaps, and it is the source of synthetic violet. Vetiver is a native of India, but the crop is widely grown in the warm lands of the Old World as well as in Louisiana and the West Indies. The sweet-scented principle which is secured from the roots of this plant is used in the manufacture of the best synthetic perfumes and in medicine.

Certain grasses are extensively used in the construction of thatched roofs. The rather crude sod huts of sheep herders in the high Andes Mountains are often covered with the coarse Ichu Grass, *Stipa ichu*. Farmers in the prairie region of North America sometimes cover their haystacks with a coarse water-shedding grass, such as Prairie Cordgrass, *Spartina pectinata*. Wheat straw has been extensively used for thatching purposes in the British Isles. Unthreshed straw is usually used for this purpose. This straw is laid on the roof in several layers to a depth of twelve to eighteen inches or even more. When it has been well prepared such a roof will last for thirty years or even longer if it is kept in good repair. Downy Chess, *Bromus tectorum* (Fig. 56), is used for thatching in some of the humid areas of the Old World. Perhaps the mose widely used and valuable of all of the thatch grasses is Cogon or Kogon Grass, *Imperata cylindrica*. This grass is grown in Africa, southeast Asia, the islands of the southwest Pacific, and in India and Burma expressly for roofing purposes. It is so well known and suited for that purpose that it is often called *thatch* grass. The grass is used for the roofing of temples and public buildings as well as for smaller houses.

Weeds are described as more or less harmful or useless plants that persist in growing where they are not wanted. Many grasses, however, are weeds. One may readily understand from this definition that almost any plant, even a species that is very useful under certain conditions, may be a weed or become a weed under certain other conditions. Botanists, in fact, recognize many weeds in nearly all of the main groups of the vegetable kingdom. There are weeds even among micro-organisms. The mycologist and the bacteriologist have great difficulty in growing the fungi or bacteria in which they are interested because of the ever-present tendency of other species of organisms to invade the cultures and so become "weeds" or *contaminants,* as they are usually called.

Weeds commonly interfere in some way with the growth of the plants that are most desired; they are undesirable and, therefore, much expense is often required to keep them out or under control. But certain worthless weeds may be beneficial to check erosion or floods, as for instance the different species that may survive the erosive influence of wind or water, after the more desirable plants have been carried away. Even the deleterious influence of certain micro-organisms when they invade and "spoil" pure cultures may, after all, be of very great value when the more complete influence of their presence is known. It was in this type of association among micro-organisms that a certain mold, *Penicillium notatum,* was found to produce the famous *penicillin,* which has lately become so valuable to medical science.

ANNUAL GRASS WEEDS

Ordinarily we think of weeds as herbaceous plants that are persistently troublesome in cultivated fields, gardens, pastures, ranges, and lawns. Almost any species of *grass* may be a weed if it persists in growing where we wish to grow something else. Even corn plants would be weeds in a wheat field and bluegrass a weed in the pansy bed or onion patch. The degree of weediness varies greatly for different species and for the same species under different environmental conditions. Annual species are likely to be less troublesome than perennial species, especially if the latter have creeping rhizomes or widely spreading root systems. Annual weeds can be easily controlled if the plants are prevented from forming their flowers or seeds. Many such species produce enormous numbers of very small seeds and, unless attempts at eradication are very general and thorough, some few plants will fruit and so will supply plenty of seeds to maintain the species. Eternal vigilance and the thorough application of the indicated remedial measures are the prices that must be paid for the control of weeds. It has been reported that weeds cause a loss of $3,000,000,000 a year to the farmers of the United States.

The weediness or the tendency to become weeds of most grasses is so mild that such species are not particularly to be dreaded. But there are certain species that qualify as really troublesome weeds. There are several annual grasses that are outstanding weeds, among which may be mentioned Downy Chess or Brome Grass, *Bromus tectorum* (Fig. 56), Ripgut Grass, *B. rigidus,* and Foxtail Chess, *B. rubens.* The Downy Chess is found practically throughout the United States except in the extreme southeast. It is especially noticeable west of the Mississippi. The relatively barren plains and overgrazed foothills and ranges of the mountains in the western states are often covered with an extensive green blanket of this grass in early summer. It is widely grazed by sheep, cattle, and horses at that time of year, and it is of much value as a forage plant on the more arid ranges. The growth of the grass varies from a few inches to a foot high. The dull green color turns to a purplish-red hue and finally to a straw color later in

Fig. 78. Chess, or Cheat is grown for hay, but it is also quite ornamental on account of its large graceful panicles with very large spikelets *(from Hitchcock)*.

Fig. 79. Barnyard Grass, a worthless weed in fields and waste places throughout the country *(from Hitchcock)*.

summer when the plants are mature and dry. The sharp, pointed callus at the base of the dry florets and the barbed awns of this grass readily penetrate one's clothing and permeat the wool of sheep and other animals. The great stands of this dry grass also constitute a major fire hazard late in summer. The Foxtail Chess and Ripgut grasses are more or less similar species, mostly of the Pacific coast states. The dry, sharp-pointed and bristly flower parts of these grasses often penetrate the soft tissues of the eye, nose, and the inside of the mouth of livestock and game animals and cause ulcerated sores there and in other parts of the alimentary canal. A tall species of Brome Grass, *Bromus secalinus* (Fig. 78), which is also called *cheat* or *chess* is often seen as a weed along roadsides and in grain fields in the northern United States. This species has been introduced from Europe.

Other annual grasses that are commonly seen as weeds in fields, meadows, pastures, and waste places are Barnyard Grass, *Echinochloa*

FIG. 80. Sandbur, the bane of every small boy on a poorly kept farm *(from Hitchcock)*.

FIG. 81. Crabgrass, or Water Grass, one of the most troublesome pests of lawns in the United States *(from Hitchcock)*.

crus-galli (Fig. 79), Mouse Barley, *Hordeum murinum,* and Little Barley, *H. pusillum.* The yellow Bristlegrass or Foxtail, *Setaria lutescens* (Fig. 82), may also be mentioned here as widespread and a very common weed of cultivated soil, especially in stubble fields, and waste places. The curious tangled, green heads of the Bur Bristlegrass, *S. verticillata,* are often seen in similar places from Rhode Island to California.

Certain annual grasses produce their flowers in finely branched, bushy, clusters that are many inches in diameter, and, at maturity this whole structure breaks off and may blow about and be caught in one's clothing. Such species are often called *Tickle-grass,* of which Tumble Tickle-grass, or Lovegrass, *Eragrostis trichodes,* and Old Witch Grass, *Panicum capillare,* are good examples. The Sandbur Grasses, such as *Cenchrus pauciflorus* and *C. tribuloides* (Fig. 80), are obnoxious because of their well-known spiny burs, inside of which one will find the flowers and seeds.

FIG. 82. Yellow Foxtail, of some value as a forage plant but mostly a weed in many places *(from Hitchcock).*

FIG. 83. Uuack Grass, or Couch-grass is a troublesome weed in fields and meadows because of its vigorous and persistent rhizomes *(from Hitchcock).*

The lawn and greensward of parks and playing fields are often invaded by troublesome grassy weeds. In this group of grasses we find, in the United States, the all too familiar Crabgrasses or Water Grasses, *Digitaria sanguinalis* (Fig. 81), and *D. ischaemum.* Either of these will ruin a fine bluegrass lawn almost before the owner notices them unless he is more alert than the average of his fellow property owners. The Annual Bluegrass, *Poa annua,* is another nasty pest of lawns. This is a really cosmopolitan species that readily makes its home even upon dry paths and drives as well as in good lawns and gardens if given half a chance.

An especially critical time to watch for the incoming of troublesome weeds is when the lawn is suffering from protracted drought. They include several grasses that seem to enjoy just that sort of an environment. The Annual Dropseed Grass, *Sporobolus neglectus,* the Hairy Brome, *Bromus tectorum,* the Windmill Grass, *Chloris verticillata,* and the Poverty Grasses, *Aristida dichotoma* and *A. oligantha,* are good examples of this type of weed. Such grasses seldom give any trouble except in a weak, poorly fertilized lawn and one that has become thinned by drought or other causes.

PERENNIAL GRASS WEEDS

There are also many perennial grasses that are weeds or that often become weeds. The most of these are species with extensive root systems and very tenacious and vigorous rhizomes or underground stems. An excellent example of this kind of weed is the world-renowned Quack Grass, *Agropyron repens* (Fig. 83). This is a wild wheatgrass which is often a very troublesome weed in cultivated fields, pastures, and other grasslands. The very active and effective propagation by means of the extensive and persistent rhizomes make of this species one of the most difficult to eradicate or control. Only a small fragment of a live rhizome is sufficient to start a new point of establishment from which the plant rapidly spreads. It is more or less ironical that this very same characteristic is often utilized by man to his great benefit as he uses this species and others of similar habits for erosion control and flood prevention in connection with soil conservation practices.

The valuable hay plant, that was originally introduced from the Mediterranean basin, and is commonly known as Johnson Grass, *Sorghum halepense* (Fig. 84), often escapes from the hay fields to invade cultivated fields and gardens. The extensive, creeping, scaly rhizomes quickly establish the plant and aid it in spreading rapidly, in spite of extremely vigorous efforts to check it. This troublesome pest has been especially obnoxious in the rich soils of the lower Mississippi states. It is also troublesome in irrigated districts where it often establishes itself along the canals and smaller ditches.

Other perennial grasses that are valuable for pasture or hay may, under certain conditions, develop to such a degree as to be weeds of first rank. The perennial Italian Ryegrass, *Lolium perenne,* is one of these. The species was introduced from Europe many years ago as a cultivated grass for meadows, pastures, and lawns. This grass frequently invades irrigated alfalfa fields in the west where it may gain the upper hand and practically eliminate the alfalfa in a few years because of its aggressive competition.

The Squirreltail Grass, or Foxtail Barley, *Hordeum jubatum,* is another common perennial weed in pastures, hay meadows, grain fields, and waste places. It is especially common throughout the Trans-Missouri country in moist saline and alkaline soils. The showy bearded

Fig. 84.   Johnson Grass, is an excellent forage grass, but it often becomes a pernicious weed on the "Black Lands" of the south; it is a close relative of the Sorghums *(from Hitchcock).*

heads of this grass are very troublesome to sheep and cattle and wild game such as deer, elk, and antelope. Serious diseases and various types of abnormalities are caused in the eyes, mouth, and intestinal tract of animals that have eaten the harsh, dry heads of this grass. The Spear Grass, or Cogon, *Imperata cylindrica,* is a tall perennial grass of the southwest Pacific and southeastern Asia that often becomes a troublesome and persistent weed. This species often invades and thoroughly establishes itself in wide areas where the tropical forests have been destroyed.

Many additional species of annual and perennial grasses that are often seen as more or less troublesome weeds could be cited. The above selections will serve to represent these large and diverse types whose importance in the varied marches of mankind is too little appreciated by the average citizen.

Tremendous savings could result if much greater and more serious effort were devoted to the control of weeds. There is an abundance of help for our citizens in this matter to be found in the numerous books on weeds, and special bulletins published by the various state agricultural experiment stations. To tolerate the wasteful and untidy presence of weeds is to contribute too much to a shiftlessness that is too often a feature of human life.

Let us strive to improve and beautify the varied course of man as he continues his march with the grasses by a more complete control of the weeds along the pathway. In this simple manner, we can aid the grasses in their contributions to the development of a more beneficial and beautiful world.

Bibliography

The following carefully selected titles, mostly from comparatively recent non-technical literature, present information relative to the material of this book. Many of these have suggested thoughts that have been used in the presentation of our story. The serious reader will find much valuable supplemental reading in these publications.

AAMODT, O. S., "Climate and Forage Crops," *U. S. Department of Agriculture Yearbook, 1941.*

ABBOTT, J. F., *Some Facts About the Sugar Research Foundation, Inc.*, New York: The Sugar Research Foundation, 1945.

ALLIN, B. W. AND FOSTER, E. A., "The Challenge of Conservation," *U. S. Department of Agriculture Yearbook, 1940.*

ALLRED, B., W., *Range Conservation Practices for the Great Plains*, U. S. Department of Agriculture Misc. Pub. No. 410, 1940.

————, *Grassland Conservation in Soil Conservation Districts*, U. S. Soil Conservation Service, Ft. Worth, Texas: 1947.

ASHLEY, W., *Bread of Our Forefathers*, New York: Oxford University Press, 1928.

BAILEY, R. W., CRADDOCK, G. W. AND CROFT, A. R., *Watershed Management for Summer Flood Control in Utah*, U. S. Department of Agriculture Misc. Pub. No. 639, 1947.

BALL, C. R., *The History and Distribution of Sorghum*, U. S. Department of Agriculture, Bu. Pt. Ind., Bul. No. 175, 1910.

BALL, C. R., *et al*, "Oats, Barley, Rye, Rice, Grains, Sorghums, Seed Flax and Buckwheat," *U. S. Department of Agriculture Yearbook, 1922.*

BALDWIN, MARK, *et al, Soil Conservation: An International Study*, New York: Columbia University Press, 1947, pp. 189.

BARNES, W. C., *The Story of the Range*, Sixty-sixth Congress, First Session, Part 6, Hearings before a sub-committee on Public Lands and Surveys, United States Senate, 1926.

BENEDIKTOV, I., "Agriculture in the Soviet Union," Washington, D. C.: *Embassy of the U.S.S.R. Information Bul.*, Vol. VI, No. 5, Jan. 15, 1946.

BENNETT, H. H., "Relation of Erosion to Vegetative Changes," *Scientific Monthly*, Vol. 55, Nov., 1932.

————, *Conservation Farming Practices and Flood Control*, U. S. Department of Agriculture Misc. Pub. 253, 1936.

————, *Soil Conservation*, New York: McGraw-Hill Book Company, 1939. pp. xvii + 933, illus.

————, "Our Soil Can Be Saved," *U. S. Department of Agriculture Yearbook, 1940.*

BENNETT, H. H. AND CHAPLINE, W. R., *Soil Erosion a National Menace*, U. S. Department of Agriculture Circ. 33, 1928.

BENNETT, H. H. AND LOWDERMILK, W. C., "General Aspects of the Soil Erosion Problem," *U. S. Department of Agriculture Yearbook, 1938.*

BENTLEY, H. L., *The Cattle Range of the Southwest,* U. S. Department of Agriculture Farmers' Bul. No. 72, 1938.

BERCAW, L. O., *Corn in the Development of the Civilization of the Americas,* (a bibliography) U. S. Bureau of Agricultural Economics, 1940.

BERGSMARK, D. R., *Economic Geography of Asia,* New York: Prentice-Hall, 1935.

BISHOP, C. W., *The Beginnings of Civilization in Eastern Asia,* Washington, D. C.: Smithsonian Institution, Ann. Rept., 1940.

————, *Origin of the Far Eastern Civilizations,* Washington, D. C.: Smithsonian Institution, Ann. Rept., 1942.

BOOKER, L. E., *et al,* "Vitamin Needs of Man," *U. S. Department of Agriculture Yearbook, 1939.*

BOURNE, G., *Nutrition and the War,* New York: The Macmillan Company, Cambridge: The University Press, 1943. pp. 148.

BOWMAN, I., *The Pioneer Fringe,* New York: American Geographical Society, Special Pub. No. 13, 1931. ix + 361, illus.

BRANDES, E. W. AND COONS, G. H., "Climatic Relations of Sugarcane and Sugar Beet," *U. S. Department of Agriculture Yearbook, 1941.*

BRANDES, E. W. AND SARTORIS, G. B., "Sugarcane: Its Origin and Improvement," *U. S. Department of Agriculture Yearbook, 1936.*

BRODY, S., "Science and Dietary Wisdom," *Scientific Monthly,* Vol. LXI, No. 3, 1945.

BROOKS, E. C., *The Story of Corn and the Westward Migration,* New York: Rand, McNally and Company, 1916.

BRUNSON, A. M., "Popcorn Breeding," *U. S. Department of Agriculture Yearbook, 1937.*

BUCK, J. L., *Land Utilization in China,* Chicago: University of Chicago Press, 1937, 3 vols.

BUREAU OF AGRICULTURAL ECONOMICS, *A Graphic Summary of Farm Crops,* U. S. Department of Agriculture Misc. Pub. No. 512, 1943.

BURTT-DAVY, J., *Maize: Its History, Cultivation, Handling, and Uses,* New York: Longmans, Green and Company, 1914. pp. xl + 831 illus.

BYERS, H. E., *et al,* "Formation of Soil," *U. S. Department of Agriculture Yearbook, 1938.*

CABLE, M., AND FRENCH, F., *The Gobi Desert,* London: Hodder and Stoughton, 1943. pp. 303, illus.

CARDON, P. V., CHAPLINE, W. R., *et al,* "Pasture and Range in Livestock Feeding," *U. S. Department of Agriculture Yearbook, 1939.*

CARLETON, M. A., *The Small Grains,* New York: The Macmillan Company, 1916.

————, *The Small Grains,* New York: The Macmillan Company, 1923. pp. xxxii + 699, illus.

CARRIER, L., *The Beginnings of Agriculture in America,* New York: McGraw-Hill Book Company, 1923. pp. xvii + 323, illus.

CARROLL, F. B., *Understanding Our Environment,* Philadelphia: Winston, 1948. pp. vii + 313, illus.

CHAPLINE, W. R. AND COOPERRIDER, C. K., "Climate and Grazing," *U. S. Department of Agriculture Yearbook, 1941.*

CHAPMAN, H. H., "The Case of the Public Range," Washington, D. C.: *American Forests,* Vol. 54, 1948.

CHASE, AGNES, *First Book of Grasses,* New York: The Macmillan Company, 1922. pp. xiii + 121, illus.

CHASE, S., *Rich Land, Poor Land: A Study of Waste in the Natural Resources of America,* New York: Whittlesey House, McGraw-Hill Book Company, 1936. pp. x + 361, illus.

CHATFIELD, C. AND ADAMS, G., *Proximate Composition of American Food Materials,* U. S. Department of Agriculture Cir. No. 549, 1940.

CHEW, A. P., "The City Man's Stake in the Land," *U. S. Department of Agriculture Yearbook, 1940.*

CHICK, H. AND COPPING, A., "Britain's National Bread," *Scientific Monthly,* Vol. LXI, No. 3, 1945.

CHILCOTT, E. F., *Preventing Soil Blowing on the Southern Great Plains,* U. S. Department of Agriculture Farmers' Bul. No. 1771, 1937.

CLAPP, E. H., *et al, The Western Range: A Great but Neglected Natural Resource,* Doc. No. 199, United States Senate, 74th Congress, 2nd Session, 1936. pp. 620, illus.

CLARK, J. A., "Improvement in Wheat," *U. S. Department of Agriculture Yearbook, 1936.*

CLARK, J. A. AND QUISENBERRY, K. S., *Distribution of the Varieties of Wheat in the United States in 1934,* U. S. Department of Agriculture Cir. No. 424, 1937.

CLARK, J. A. AND BAYLES, B. B., *Classification of Wheat Varieties Grown in the United States in 1939,* U. S. Department of Agriculture Tech. Bul. No. 795, 1942.

COLE, J. S., "The Farmer and the Soil," *U. S. Department of Agriculture Yearbook, 1938.*

COLLIER, J. E., "Artesian Water and Australia's Pastoral Industry," *Scientific Monthly,* Feb., 1945.

COLLINS, G. N., "Notes on the Agricultural History of Corn," Washington: *American Historical Association, Ann. Rept. for the year 1919,* 1923.

COOK, R., "A Chronology of Genetics," *U. S. Department of Agriculture Yearbook, 1937.*

COOPERRIDER, C. K., AND HENDRICKS, B. A., *Soil Erosion and Stream Flow on the Range and Forest Lands of the Upper Rio Grande Watershed in Relation to Land Resources and Human Welfare,* U. S. Department of Agriculture Tech. Bul. No. 547, 1937.

COPELAND, E. B., *Rice,* New York: The Macmillan Company, 1924. pp. xiv + 352, illus.

CRESSEY, G. B., "Foundations of Chinese Life," *Economic Geography,* Vol. XV, 1939.

————, *Asia's Lands and Peoples,* New York: McGraw-Hill Book Company, 1944. pp. xi + 605, illus.

CRIST, R., "Life on the Llanos of Venezuela," Philadelphia: *Bul. Geographic Society of Philadelphia,* Vol. 35, No. 2, 1937.

DAVIES, R. A., *Soviet Asia,* New York: Dial Press, 1942.

DAVIES, W., "The Grasslands of the Argentine and Patagonia," Aberystwyth: *Imp. Bur. Pasture and Forage Crops,* 1940.

DAYTON, W. A., *et al, Range Plant Handbook,* Washington: U. S. Department of Agriculture, Forest Service, 1937. pp. 1500 circa, illus.

EDWARDS, E. E., "American Agriculture: The First 300 Years," *U. S. Department of Agriculture Yearbook, 1940.*

ELLIOTT, F. F., *et al,* "The Farmer's Changing World," *U. S. Department of Agriculture Yearbook, 1940.*

ENLOW, C. R. AND MUSGRAVE, G. W., "Grass and Other Thick-growing Vegetation in Erosion Control," *U. S. Department of Agriculture Yearbook, 1938.*

ESTABROOK, L. M., *Agricultural Survey of South America—Argentina and Paraguay,* U. S. Department of Agriculture Bul. No. 1409, 1926.

EVANS, M. W., "Improvement of Timothy," *U. S. Department of Agriculture Yearbook, 1937.*

FINCH, V. C. AND BAKER, O. E., *Geography of the World's Agriculture,* U. S. Department of Agriculture, Office of Farm Management, 1917.

FRACKER, S. B., *et al, Improving Pastures and Grasslands for the Northeastern States,* U. S. Department of Agriculture Misc. Pub. 590, 1946.

FURNAS, C. C. AND COOK, C., *Man, Bread, and Destiny,* New York: Reynal and Hitchcock, 1937.

GILES, D., *Singing Valleys: The Story of Corn,* New York: Random House, 1940.

GOLDENWEISER, E. A. AND BALL, J. S., *Pasture Land on Farms in the United States,* U. S. Department of Agriculture Bul. No. 626, 1918.

GOODWIN, D. C. AND JOHNSTONE, P. H., "A Brief Chronology of American Agricultural History," *U. S. Department of Agriculture Yearbook, 1940.*

GREAVES, J. E., *The Minerals of Wheat and Their Relationship to Human and Animal Nutrition,* Logan: Utah Agricultural Experiment Station Cir. No. 113, 1940.

GREGORY, J. S. AND SHAVE, D. W., *The U. S. S. R.: A Geographic Survey,* New York: John Wiley and Sons, 1944. pp. 636, illus.

GREGORY, W. K., "Australia: The Story of a Continent," *Natural History,* New York: Am. Mus. Natl. Hist., Oct., 1944.

GRIFFITHS, D., *et al, Native Pasture Grasses of the United States,* U. S. Department of Agriculture Bul. No. 201, 1915.

GUSTAFSON, A. F., *et al, Conservation in the United States,* Ithaca, New York: Comstock Publishing Company, 1939. pp. xix + 445, illus.

HACKEL, E., *The True Grasses,* Translated from the German by F. Lamson-Scribner, Westminster: A. Constable and Company, 1896. pp. 288, illus.

HAMBIDGE, G., "Soils and Men: A Summary," *U. S. Department of Agriculture Yearbook, 1938.*

————, "Food and Life," *U. S. Department of Agriculture Yearbook, 1939.*

————, "Farmers in a Changing World: A Summary," *U. S. Department of Agriculture Yearbook, 1940.*

————, "Climate and Man: A Summary," *U. S. Department of Agriculture Yearbook, 1941.*

HAMILTON, C. L., *Terracing for Soil and Water Conservation,* U. S. Department of Agriculture Farmers' Bul. No. 1789, 1938.

HARDING, T. S., "Science and Agricultural Policy," *U. S. Department of Agriculture Yearbook, 1940.*

HARDY, M. E., *The Geography of Plants,* Oxford: The Clarendon Press, 1920. pp. iv + 327, illus., maps.

————, *A Junior Plant Geography,* Oxford: The Clarendon Press, 1924. pp. 192, illus.

HARLAN, H. V., *Barley: Culture, Uses and Varieties*, U. S. Department of Agriculture Farmers' Bul. No. 1464, 1925.

HARLAN, H. V. AND MARTINI, M. L., "Problems and Results of Barley Breeding," *U. S. Department of Agriculture Yearbook, 1936*.

HARSHBERGER, J. W., *Phytogeographic Survey of North America*, New York: G. E. Stechert and Company, 1911. Vol. 13 of *Die Vegetation der Erde*, Engler and Drude. pp. lxiii + 790, illus., maps.

HAVILAND, M. D., *Forest, Steppe and Tundra*, London: The University Press, New York: The Macmillan Company, 1926. pp. 218, illus.

HAYES, H. K. AND GARBER, R. J., *Breeding Crop Plants*, New York: McGraw-Hill Book Company, 1927. pp. xxii + 438, illus.

HILDEBRAND, E. M., "War on Weeds," *Science*, Vol. 103, No. 2677, 1946.

HILL, A. F., *Economic Botany: A Textbook of Useful Plants and Plant Products*, New York: McGraw-Hill Book Company, 1937. pp. vii + 592, illus.

HITCHCOCK, A. S., *A Textbook of Grasses*, New York: The Macmillan Company, 1914. pp. xvii + 276, illus.

————, *Manual of the Grasses of the United States*, U. S. Department of Agriculture Misc. Pub. No. 200, 1935. pp. 1040, illus.

————, *The Genera of Grasses of the United States*, U. S. Department of Agriculture Bul. No. 772, 1920, revised Ed., 1936.

HOLMES, MACDONALD, "The Australian Geographical Environment," *The Australian Geographic*, Vol. 2, No. 1, 1933.

HOOVER, M. M., *Native and Adapted Grasses for Conservation of Soil Moisture in the Great Plains and Western States*, U. S. Department of Agriculture Farmers' Bul. No. 1812, 1939.

HUBBARD, G. D., *Geography of Europe*, New York: Appleton-Century Company, 1937.

HUGHES, H. D. AND HENSON, E. R., *Crop Production*, New York: The Macmillan Company, 1935. pp. 750, illus.

HUNTINGTON, ELLSWORTH, *Mainsprings of Civilization*, New York: John Wiley and Sons, 1945. pp xii + 660, illus.

HUTCHESON, T. B. AND WOLFE, T. K., *The Production of Field Crops*, New York: McGraw-Hill Book Company, 1924. pp. xv + 499, illus.

HUTCHESON, T. B., *et al*, *The Production of Field Crops*, New York: McGraw-Hill Book Company, 1936.

JACKS, G. V. AND WHYTE, R. O., *Vanishing Lands: A World Survey of Soil Erosion*, New York: Doubleday, Doran and Company, 1939. pp. xvi + 332, illus.

JACOB, H. E., *Six Thousand Years of Bread*, Garden City, New York: Doubleday, Doran and Company, 1944. pp. xiv + 399, illus.

JENKINS, M. T., "Corn Improvement," *U. S. Department of Agriculture Yearbook, 1936*.

————, "Influence of Climate and Wealth on Growth of Corn," *U. S. Department of Agriculture Yearbook, 1941*.

JONES, J. W., *Rice Experiments at the Riggs Rice Field Station in California*, U. S. Department of Agriculture Bul. No. 1155, 1923.

————, *How to Grow Rice in the Sacramento Valley*, U. S. Department of Agriculture Farmers' Bul. No. 1240, 1924.

————, "Improvement in Rice," *U. S. Department of Agriculture Yearbook, 1936*.

JONES, J. W., *et al*, *Rice Culture in the Southern States*, U. S. Department of Agriculture Farmers' Bul. No. 1808, 1938.

JONES, L. G. AND THOMPSON, L. M., *Soil Erosion and Its Control*, College Station, Texas: Department of Agronomy, Agr. and Mech. Col. of Texas, 1941.

KELL, W. V., "Strip Cropping," *U. S. Department of Agriculture Yearbook, 1938.*

KELLER, B. A., "Distribution of Vegetation on the Plains of Southern Russia," *Journal of Ecology*, Vol. XV, 1927.

KELLOGG, C. E., "Soil and Society," *U. S. Department of Agriculture Yearbook, 1938.*

————, "Climate and Soil," *U. S. Department of Agriculture Yearbook, 1941.*

KENOYER, L. A., "Plant Life of British India," *Scientific Monthly*, Vol. XVIII, 1924.

KENT, G., "A Farmer Bags a Million Dollars," (hybrid corn), *The Country Home Magazine*, Aug., 1938.

————, "A Farmer Bags a Million Dollars," (hybrid corn) , *The Reader's Digest*, Sept., 1938.

KINCH, R., *Weeds in Nebraska*, Lincoln: Nebraska State Department of Agriculture and Inspection, Bul. No. 101, pp. 238, rev. ed., 1936, illus.

KING, F. H., *Farmers of Forty Centuries for China and Japan*, New York: Harcourt, Brace and Company, 1926.

KLAGES, K. H. W., *Ecological Crop Geography*, New York: The Macmillan Company, 1942. pp. xvii + 615, illus.

KLIMM, L. E. AND STARKEY, O. P., *Introductory Economic Geography*, New York: Harcourt, Brace and Company, 1940. pp. vi + 501, illus.

LEIGHTY, C. E., *et al*, "The Corn Crop," *U. S. Department of Agriculture Yearbook, 1921.*

LIVELY, C. E. AND TAEUBER, C., *Rural Migration in the United States*, U. S. Works Progress Administration, Div. Res., Res. Monog. No. 19, 1939. pp. 192, illus.

LIVINGSTON, B. E. AND SHREVE, F., *The Distribution of Vegetation in the United States as Related to Climatic Conditions*, Washington, D. C.: Carnegie Institution Pub. No. 284, 1921.

LORD, RUSSELL, *To Hold This Soil*, U. S. Department of Agriculture Misc. Pub. No. 321, 1938.

LOWDERMILK, W. C., "Erosion in the Orient as Related to Soil Conservation in America," *Journal of the American Society of Agronomy*, Vol. 21, 1929.

LOWDERMILK, W. C. AND WICKES, D. R., "China and America Against Soil Erosion," *Scientific Monthly*, Vol. LVI, 1943.

LYON, T. L. AND BUCKMAN, H. O., *The Nature and Properties of Soils*, New York: The Macmillan Company, 1943. pp. xi + 499, illus. 4th Ed.

MANGELSDORF, D. C. AND REEVES, R. J., *The Origin of Indian Corn and Its Relatives.* College Station: Texas Agricultural Experiment Station Bul. No. 574, 1939.

MARBUT, C. F., "Russia and the United States in the World's Wheat Market," *The Geographical Review*, Vol. 21, 1931.

MARTIN, J. H. "Sorghum Improvement," *U. S. Department of Agriculture Yearbook, 1936.*

————, "Climate and Sorghum," *U. S. Department of Agriculture Yearbook, 1941.*

MARTIN, J. H. AND STEPHENS, J. C., "The Culture and Use of Sorghums for Forage," U. S. Department of Agriculture, Farmers' Bul. No. 1844, 1940.

McDOUGALL, E. J., *Report on Bread in Several European Countries*, Bul. Health Organization, League of Nations 8, No. 3, Washington, D. C., 1939.

MERRILL, E. D., *Plant Life of the Pacific World,* New York: The Macmillan Company, 1945. pp. xv + 295, illus.

MICHAEL, L. G., "The Soviet Ukraine: Its People and Agriculture," *Foreign Agriculture,* Vol. III, 1939.

MIDDLETON, H. E., *Properties of Soils Which Influence Erosion,* U. S. Department of Agriculture Tech. Bul. No. 178, 1930.

MIKHAILOV, N., *Land of the Soviets,* New York: Furman, 1939.

MITCHELL, HELEN S., *et al,* "Human Food Requirements," *U. S. Department of Agriculture Yearbook, 1939.*

MONTGOMERY, E. G., *The Corn Crops: A Discussion of Maize, Kafirs, and Sorghums as Grown in the United States and Canada,* New York: The Macmillan Company, 1913.

MORRISON, G., "Hybrid Corn: Science in Practice," *Economic Botany,* Vol. I, No. 1, 1947.

MUENSCHER, W. C., *Weeds,* New York: The Macmillan Company, 1935, pp. xxii 577, illus.

MURNEEK, A. E., "Vitamins in Our Food," *Science,* Vol. 100, No. 2608, Dec., 1944.

MYERS, J. G., "Notes on the Vegetation of the Venezuelan Llanos," *Journal of Ecology,* Vol. 21, 1933.

NORTH, H. F. A. AND ODLAND, T. E., *Putting Green Grasses and Their Management,* Rhode Island Agriculture Experiment Station Bul. No. 245, 1934.

OSBORN, F., *Our Plundered Planet,* Boston: Little, Brown and Company, 1948, pp. 217.

OSBORNE, T. B., *The Proteins of the Wheat Kernel,* Washington, D. C.: The Carnegie Institution, 1907.

OSBORNE, T. B. AND MENDEL, L. B., "The Nutritive Value of the Wheat Kernel and Its Milling Products," *Journal of Biological Chemistry,* Vol. 37, p. 557, 1919.

PENROSE, E. F., *Food Supply and Raw Materials in Japan,* Chicago: University of Chicago Press, 1929.

PERCIVAL, J., *The Wheat Plant: A Monograph,* New York: E. P. Dutton and Company, 1921. pp. 463, illus.

PHILLIPS, E. P., *An Introduction to the Study of South African Grasses,* South Africa: Central News Agency, 1931. pp. 224, illus.

PIPER, C. V., *Forage Plants and Their Culture,* New York: The Macmillan Company, 1920. pp. xv + 618, illus.

——————, *Important Cultivated Grasses,* U. S. Department of Agriculture Farmers' Bul. No. 1254, 1922.

——————, *Forage Plants and Their Culture,* New York: The Macmillan Company, 1939. pp. xxiv + 671, illus.

POOLE, C. F., "Improvement of Sweet Corn," *U. S. Department of Agriculture Yearbook, 1937.*

POOL, R. J., "White Man versus the Prairie," *Science,* Vol. 91, No. 2351, 1940.

——————, *Flowers and Flowering Plants,* New York: McGraw-Hill Book Company, 1941. pp. xiv + 428, illus.

——————, "Vegetation of the Sandhills of Nebraska," *The University of Minnesota Botanical Studies,* Vol. 4, Part 3, 1914.

RAMSER, C. E., *Prevention of Erosion of Farm Lands by Terracing,* U. S. Department of Agriculture Bul. No. 512, 1917.

————, *Gullies: How to Control and Reclaim Them,* U. S. Department of Agriculture Farmers' Bul. No. 1234, 1922.

RATHER, H. C., *Field Crops,* New York: McGraw-Hill Book Company, 1942. pp. ix + 454, illus.

REED, W. W., "The Climates of the World," *U. S. Department of Agriculture Yearbook, 1941.*

RENNER. G. T., "A Famine Zone in Africa: The Sudan," *The Geographical Review,* Vol. 16, 1926.

RICHEY, F. D., "The What and How of Hybrid Corn," U. S. Department of Agriculture Farmers' Bul. No. 1744, 1935.

ROBBINS, W. W., *The Botany of Crop Plants,* Philadelphia: P. Blakiston's Son and Company, 1931. pp. xxi + 674, illus., 3rd Ed.

ROBERTSON, C. J., *World Sugar Production and Consumption: An Economic and Geographical Study,* London: J. Bale, Sons and Danielsson, 1934.

RUSSELL, R. J., "Climatic Change Through the Ages," *U. S. Department of Agriculture Yearbook, 1941.*

RUTTER, W. P., *Wheat-growing in Canada, the United States and the Argentine Including Comparisons with Other Areas,* London: A. and C. Black, 1911. pp. x + 315, diag. and charts.

SALMON, S. C., "Climate and Small Grains," *U. S. Department of Agriculture Yearbook, 1941.*

SALMON, S. C. AND TAYLOR, J. W., *Growing Wheat in Eastern United States,* U. S. Department of Agriculture Farmers' Bul. No. 1817, 1939.

SAMPSON, A. W., *Important Range Plants: Their Life History and Forage Value,* U. S. Department of Agriculture Bul. No. 545, 1917.

————, *Range and Pasture Management,* New York: John Wiley and Sons, 1923. pp. xix + 421, illus.

————, *Native American Forage Plants,* New York: John Wiley and Sons, 1924. pp. xxv + 435, illus.

SAUER, C. O., *et al,* "Climate and Agricultural Settlement," *U. S. Department of Agriculture Yearbook, 1941.*

SARVIS, J. T. AND STEVENS, O. A., *et al, Grass,* Fargo: North Dakota Agricultural Experiment Station Bul. No. 300, 1941.

SCHIMPER, A. F. W., *Plant-Geography: Upon a Physiological Basis,* Oxford: Oxford University Press, 1903. Translated by W. R. Fisher. pp. xxx + 840, illus., maps.

SEARS, P. B., *Deserts on the March,* Norman: The University of Oklahoma Press, 1935. pp. 231, 2nd Ed. 1947.

————, *This Is Our World,* Norman: The University of Oklahoma Press, 1937. pp ix + 292, illus.

————, *Life and Environment,* New York: Teachers College, Columbia University, 1939. pp. xi + 175.

SEMPLE, A. T. AND VINALL, H. N., *et al, A Pasture Handbook,* U. S. Department of Agriculture Misc. Pub. No. 194, 1934.

SHALLENBERGER, J. H., *Wheat Requirements of Europe,* U. S. Department of Agriculture Tech. Bul. No. 535, 1936.

SHANTZ, H. L., "The Natural Vegetation of the Great Plains Region," *Ann. Assoc. Am. Geogr.,* Vol. 13, 1923.

————, "Plants as Soil Indicators," *U. S. Department of Agriculture Yearbook, 1938.*

SHANTZ, H. L. AND MARBUT, C. F., *The Vegetation and Soils of Africa,* New York: National Research Council and the American Geographical Society, Res. Ser. 13, 1923.

SHARRITT, GRACE V., "Breadbasket Seasoned with Sage," Washington, D. C.: American Forestry Association, *American Forests,* Vol. 51, No. 9, Sept. 1945.

SHEPARD, WARD, *Food or Famine,* New York: The Macmillan Company, 1945. pp. x + 225.

SHERMAN, H. C. AND PEARSON, C. S., *Modern Bread from the Viewpoint of Nutrition,* New York: The Macmillan Company, 1942. pp. vi + 118.

SHULL, G. H., "Hybrid Seed Corn," *Science,* Vol. 103, No. 2679, 1946.

SMITH, L. B. *The Vegetation of Brazil: Plants and Plant Science in South America,* Waltham, Massachusetts: Chronica Botanica Company, 1945. pp. 297 + 302.

SPRAGUE, H. S., *Better Lawns for Homes and Parks,* New York: Whittlesey House, McGraw-Hill Book Company, 1940. pp. xiv + 205, illus.

STANFORD, E. L., *Economic Plants,* New York: D. Appleton-Century, 1934. pp. xxiii + 571, illus.

STEEL, K., "Revolution in the Corn Belt," *Harpers Magazine,* August, 1945.

————, "Revolution in the Corn Belt," (hybrid corn), *The Reader's Digest,* Vol. XLVII, Sept., 1945.

STEWART, GEORGE, et al, *Reseeding Range Lands of the Intermountain Region,* U. S. Department of Agriculture Farmers' Bul. No. 1823, 1939.

STEIBERLING, H. K., "Food Habits: Old and New," *U. S. Department of Agriculture Yearbook, 1939.*

————, "Better Nutrition as a National Goal," *U. S. Department of Agriculture Yearbook, 1939.*

STODDART, L. A. AND SMITH, A. D., *Range Management,* New York: McGraw-Hill Book Company, 1943. pp. xii + 547, illus.

STRONG, A. L., *The Soviets Conquer Wheat,* New York: Henry Holt and Company, 1931.

SYCKES, D. C., *Cattle Raising in Argentina,* Trade Information Bul. 647, U. S. Department of Commerce, 1929.

TAGGART, W. G. AND SIMONS, E. C., *A Brief Discussion of the History of Sugar Cane,* Baton Rouge: Louisiana State Department of Agriculture and Immigration, 1939.

TANNEHILL, I. R., *Drought: Its Causes and Effects,* Princeton, N. J.: Princeton University Press, 1946. pp. 264, fig. 118, tables 5.

TAYLOR, A. E., "Rye in Its Relation to Wheat," *Wheat Studies of the Food Research Institute,* Vol. 4, No. 5, San Francisco: Standford University Press, 1928.

————, "The Place of Wheat in the Diet," *Wheat Studies of the Food Research Institute,* Vol. 5, No. 4, San Francisco: Stanford University Press, 1929.

TAYLOR, C. C., *Agriculture in Southern Africa,* U. S. Department of Agriculture Tech. Bul. No. 466, 1935.

TAYLOR, C. C., et al, "The Nation and the Soil," *U. S. Department of Agriculture Yearbook, 1938.*

TAYLOR, GRIFFITH, "Agricultural Regions in Australia," *Economic Geography,* Vol. 6, 1930.

————, "The Soils of Australia in Relation to Topography and Climate," *The Geographical Review,* Vol. 23, 1933.

————, "The Distribution of Pasture in Australia," *The Geographical Review,* Vol. XXVII, No. 2, April, 1937.

THROCKMORTON, R. I. AND COMPTON, L. L., *Soil Erosion by Wind,* Topeka: Kansas State Board of Agriculture Rept., Dec., 1937.

TIMOSHENKO, V. P., "The Danube Basin as a Producer and Exporter of Wheat," *Wheat Studies of the Food Research Institute,* Vol. 6, No. 5, San Francisco: Stanford University Press, 1930.

————, "Agricultural Russia and the Wheat Problem," San Francisco: Stanford University Press, 1932.

————, "Russia as a Producer and Exporter of Wheat," *Wheat Studies of the Food Research Institute,* Vol. 8, San Francisco: Stanford University Press, 1932.

TOWER, W. S., "The Pampa of Argentina," *The Geographical Review,* Vol. 5, 1918.

TULAIKOV, N. M., "Agriculture in the Dry Region of the U. S. S. R.," *Economic Geography,* Vol. VI, 1930.

TURNER, F., *Australian Grasses,* Sydney: Charles Potter, 1895, pp. 63, illus.

UTZ, E. J., "The Coordinated Approach to Soil Erosion Control," *U. S. Department of Agriculture Yearbook, 1938.*

VAN VALKENBURG, S., "Agricultural Regions of Asia: India," *Economic Geography,* Vol. IX, 1933.

VERDOORN, F., *Plants and Plant Science in South America,* Waltham, Massachusetts: Chronica Botanica Company, 1945. pp. xxxvii + 381, illus.

VINALL, H. N., *Sudan Grass,* U. S. Department of Agriculture Farmers' Bul. No. 1126, 1935.

VINALL, H. N., *et al, Identification, History, and Distribution of Common Sorghum Varieties,* U. S. Department of Agriculture Tech. Bul. No. 506, 1936.

VINALL, H. N. AND HEIN, M. A., "Breeding Miscellaneous Grasses," *U. S. Department of Agriculture Yearbook, 1937.*

WALLACE, H. A. AND BRESSMAN, E. N., *Corn and Corn Growing,* Des Moines: Wallace Publishing Company, 1923.

WAKSMAN, S. A., "The Living Soil," *Soil Conservation,* Vol. 3, pp. 173–177, Jan., 1938.

WEATHERWAX, P., *The Story of the Maize Plant,* Chicago: The University of Chicago Press, 1923.

WEAVER, J. E., "North American Prairie," *The American Scholar,* Vol. 13, No. 3, 1944.

WEAVER, J. E. AND FITZPATRICK, T. J., "The Prairie," *Ecological Monographs,* Vol. 4, No. 2, Ecol. Soc. Am., 1934. pp. 182, illus.

WELLS, O. V., "Agriculture Today: An Appraisal of the Agricultural Problem," *U. S. Department of Agriculture Yearbook, 1940.*

WENGER, L. E., *Buffalo Grass,* Manhattan: Kansas Agricultural Experiment Station Bul. No. 321, 1943.

WENTWORTH, E. N., *America's Sheep Trails: History and Personalities,* Ames: Iowa State College Press, 1948. pp. 667.

WHITBECK, R. H. AND WILLIAMS, F. E., *Economic Geography of South America,* New York: McGraw-Hill Book Company, 1940. pp. xi + 469.

WICKIZER, V. D. AND BENNETT, M. K., "The Rice Economy of Monsoon Asia," *Food Research Institute,* San Francisco: Stanford University Press, 1941.

WIGGANS, R. G., *A Classification of the Cultivated Varieties of Barley,* Ithaca: Cornell University Agricultural Experiment Station Memoir No. 46, 1921.

WISSLER, CLARK, "Rice as a World Food," New York: *Natural History,* American Museum of Natural History, Jan., 1946.

WOOD, I. D., *Inexpensive Methods of Gully Control,* Lincoln: Nebraska Agricultural Experiment Station Extension Cir. No. 741, 1933.

WORKING, H., "The Changing World Wheat Situation," *Wheat Studies of the Food Research Institute,* Vol. 6, No. 10, San Francisco: Stanford University Press, 1930.

WRIGHT, C. P., "India as a Producer and Exporter of Wheat," *Wheat Studies of the Food Research Institute,* Vol. 3, No. 8, San Francisco: Stanford University Press, 1927.

ZIMMERMANN, E. W., *World Resources and Industries,* New York: Harper and Company, 1933.

Index